CAROL PRAISE

WORDS E

Edited
Michael Perry (Words) and
with
Norman Warren and Noël Tredinnick

Marshall Pickering

Marshall Morgan & Scott,
3 Beggarwood Lane, Basingstoke, Hants RG23 7LP

Copyright details will be found with each item, and further information at the sections 'Copyright' and 'Legal Information'. Every effort has been made to trace copyright holders and obtain permission; the publishers would welcome details of any error or omission, which will be corrected in future reprints.

First published in 1987 by Marshall Morgan & Scott Publications Ltd., part of the Marshall Pickering Holdings Group, a subsidiary of the Zondervan Corporation.

British Library Cataloguing in Publication Data
Carol praise – Words Edition
   1. Carols, English
   I. Perry, Michael   II. Peacock, David

   ISBN 0 551 014539

Text set by Barnes Music Engraving Ltd., East Sussex.
Printed in Great Britain by Hazell Watson & Viney Limited, Aylesbury, Bucks

CONTENTS

* Numbers only. These indexes appear in full in the Music Edition of Carol
Praise, along with the following additional facilities:

Using 'Carol Praise'
Index to authors, originators and adaptors of texts
Index to composers, arrangers and sources of tunes
Index to carols suitable for SATB singing
Index to carols with descants and other vocal arrangements
Index to carols arranged as rounds
Index to response carols
Index to carols with instrumental parts
Index to seasonal hymns
Index to seasonal worship songs
Index to carols based on folk tunes or other national tunes
Index to new carols set to existing tunes
Index to carols particularly suitable for children

1

Ivor Golby
© A & C Black Limited †

1 A baby was born in Bethlehem,
   a baby was born in Bethlehem,
   a baby was born in Bethlehem –
   it was Jesus Christ, our Lord.
       Gloria, gloria in excelcis Deo;
       Gloria, gloria, sing glory to God on high!

2 They laid him in a manger . . .
   where the oxen feed on hay.
       Gloria, gloria . . .

3 Some shepherds heard the glad tidings . . .
   from an angel in the sky.
       Gloria, gloria . . .

4 They left their flocks a-sleeping . . .
   and hurried to Bethlehem.
       Gloria, gloria . . .

5 Three wise men came from far lands . . .
   they were guided by a star.
       Gloria, gloria . . .

6 They laid their gifts before him . . .
   and worshipped on bended knee.
       Gloria, gloria . . .

7 Then everybody be happy . . .
   on the birthday of our Lord!
       Gloria, gloria . . .

2

Bernadette Farrell
© Magnificat Music †

   Bread of life, hope of the world,
   Jesus Christ our brother:
   feed us now, give us life,
   lead us to one another.

1 A child is born for us,
   a son is given to us;
   in our midst Christ our Lord and God
   comes as one who serves.
       Bread of life . . .

2 With our own eyes we see,
   with our own ears we hear
   the salvation of all the world,
   God's incarnate Word.
       Bread of life . . .

3 You are the hope of all,
   promised since time began,
   radiant light in our darkness,
   truth to set us free.
       Bread of life . . .

3/4

From Isaiah 9
© Pearl Beasley

1 A child is born for us today,
   a son to us is given;
   the saviour comes to guide our way
   and lead us up to heaven.
       They'll call him 'Wonderful',
       heavenly 'Counsellor'.
   We'll call him 'Jesus'.

2 He comes to be the 'Prince of peace',
   to all the world a friend;
   his mighty love will never cease,
   his kingdom will not end.
       They'll call him 'Mighty God',
       'Eternal Father'.
   We'll call him 'Jesus'.

3 On those who walk the darkest way
   has dawned a shining light
   far brighter than the brightest day,
   a great and glorious sight.
       O come, Emmanuel,
       our God, be with us!
   O come, Lord Jesus!

5

From the Danish
© Michael Perry / Jubilate Hymns

1 A child is born in Bethlehem,
       Sing nowell, sing nowell!
   the royal flower to David's stem.
       Alleluia, alleluia!

2 Sing praises through the whole wide earth,
       Sing nowell, sing nowell!
   for Mary gives the saviour birth.
       Alleluia, alleluia!

3 He lies within a manger bare,
       Sing nowell, sing nowell!
   and shepherds kneel to worship there.
       Alleluia, alleluia!

4 He comes to be our hope of peace,
       Sing nowell, sing nowell!
   to bring imprisoned souls release.
       Alleluia, alleluia!

5 Our guilt has found a certain cure,
       Sing nowell, sing nowell!
   for Christ makes our salvation sure.
       Alleluia, alleluia!

6

After Germanus (c.634–732)
J.M. Neale (1818–1866)
© in this version Word & Music / Jubilate Hymns

1 A great and mighty wonder:
   redemption drawing near!
   the virgin bears the infant,
   the prince of peace is here!
       Repeat the hymn again:
       'To God on high be glory,
       and peace on earth. Amen.'

2 The Word becomes incarnate
   and yet remains on high;
   the shepherds hear the anthem
   as glory fills the sky.
       Repeat the hymn . . .

3 The angels sing the story:
   awake, O distant lands!
   rejoice, you hills and valleys;
   you oceans, clap your hands!
       Repeat the hymn . . .

4 He comes to save all nations:
let all now hear his word!
approach and bring him worship,
the saviour and the Lord!
  Repeat the hymn . . .

7

Traditional
© in this version Word & Music / Jubilate Hymns

1 A child this day is born,
a child of high renown;
most worthy of a sceptre –
a sceptre and a crown.

2 Good news the shepherds heard,
who watched their flock and fold;
the angel that appeared to them
of God's salvation told.

3 The angel host proclaimed
good-will and peace on earth;
for God's redeeming love was shown
in Jesus' holy birth.

4 They praised the Lord our God,
our great celestial King:
now 'Glory in the highest heaven!'
let all creation sing.

5 And what the angel said,
did now in truth appear;
at Bethlehem they found the child,
laid in a manger there.

6 Then glory be to God
who reigns supreme on high;
with glad thanksgiving, worthy praise,
and joyful melody!

7 Glad tidings sing to all,
glad tidings all shall say,
because the King of all kings
was born on Christmas Day.

8

© Michael Walker

1 A messenger named Gabriel
came to the land of Israel;
and he proclaimed that Mary's son
was God's messiah, holy One.
  O Jesus Christ, strong Son of God,
  once born for us at Bethlehem:
  we listen to the angels' song
  and worship you for ever.

2 Angelic hosts of God most high
with radiant glory fill the sky;
enraptured voices joyful sing
to welcome Christ, the new-born king.
  O Jesus Christ . . .

3 In awesome fear and bitter cold
the shepherds huddle in their fold;
then since the message is for them
they make their way to Bethlehem.
  O Jesus Christ . . .

4 Within the sacred stable-shrine
they see the holy child divine;
the manger stands amidst the straw,
and humble folk their God adore.
  O Jesus Christ . . .

5 Since then have passed two thousand years
of human misery and tears;
yet Christ alone can bring release:
he loves us still – the Prince of peace.
  O Jesus Christ . . .

9

© Timothy Dudley-Smith †

1 A song was heard at Christmas
to wake the midnight sky;
a saviour's birth, and peace on earth,
and praise to God on high.
The angels sang at Christmas
with all the hosts above,
and still we sing the newborn King,
his glory and his love.

2 A star was seen at Christmas,
a herald and a sign,
that all might know the way to go
to find the child divine.
The wise men watched at Christmas
in some far eastern land,
and still the wise in starry skies
discern their Maker's hand.

3 A tree was grown at Christmas,
a sapling green and young;
no tinsel bright with candlelight
upon its branches hung.
But he who came at Christmas
our sins and sorrows bore,
and still we name his tree of shame
our life for evermore.

4 A child was born at Christmas
when Christmas first began;
the Lord of all a baby small,
the Son of God made man.
For love is ours at Christmas,
and life and light restored,
and so we praise through endless days
the Saviour, Christ the Lord.

10

© Angela Draper

1 A star in the sky
led the Magi on their way,
a star in the sky
led them onward night and day;
then at last it came to stay
  over the town of Bethlehem.
  Sing alleluia, sing alleluia,
  sing out a song of praise;
  alleluia, sing out a song of praise –
  Christ is born in Bethlehem.

2 Gold, incense and myrrh
   were the gifts they offered there,
   gold, incense and myrrh,
   given with a reverent care:
   costly treasures they did share,
        worshipping Christ in Bethlehem.
   Sing alleluia, sing alleluia,
   sing out a song of praise;
   alleluia, sing out a song of praise –
   Christ is born in Bethlehem.

3 May Christ be our light –
   with us evermore to stay,
   may Christ be our light
   guiding us upon our way:
   bring us home to God we pray,
        Christ who was born in Bethlehem.
   Sing alleluia . . .

11 © Elizabeth Cosnett

1 Across the desert sands,
   between the forest trees,
   through frozen wastes and fertile lands
   and over swelling seas;
   by villages and towns,
   rough path and winding road,
   by craggy peaks and rolling downs
   I bear a precious load:
        Gold of the world's wealth,
        incense for worship,
        myrrh meaning sorrow,
        love beyond telling.

2 A track that shepherds tread,
   a half-remembered song,
   a star that glimmers gold and red –
   they're drawing me along;
   and when the journey's done
   I hope to meet my king
   and lay before him one by one
   the gifts I come to bring:
        Gold of the . . .

3 I've never seen the place,
   no map describes the way,
   but still I trust that by God's grace
   I shall not go astray;
   my Lord will show no scorn
   nor turn away from me,
   but gladly take what I have borne
   so far, so wearily:
        Gold of the . . .

4 Now come, O come with me,
   all you whose hearts are stirred,
   together we shall surely see
   the light of God's own word!
   And as we go we'll raise
   with all our might and main
   a pilgrim carol full of praise,
   a tender, sweet refrain:
        Gold of the . . .

12
Dave Moody

   All hail, king Jesus; all hail, Emmanuel,
   King of kings, Lord of lords,
        bright morning Star!
   And throughout eternity I'll sing your praises –
   and I'll reign with you throughout eternity.

13

1 All heaven rings with joyful songs
   as angels tell the story
   of one who comes to right our wrongs
   and take us up to glory.

2 The silent earth is filled with awe
   and mortal men stand trembling,
   for God is found among the poor,
   our very selves resembling.

3 The Lord is born this holy day
   of Mary, virgin mother,
   God's child of grace, his perfect way,
   our saviour and our brother.

4 Come, Christians, greet the living Word,
   ascribe him truth and merit;
   let heaven and earth with one accord
   praise Father, Son and Spirit!

14
After P Gerhardt (1607–1676)
C Winkworth (1827–1878)

1 All my heart this night rejoices,
        as I hear,
        far and near,
   sweetest angel voices.
   'Christ is born!' their choirs are singing,
        till the air
        everywhere
   now with joy is ringing.

2 Listen! from a humble manger
        comes the call,
        'One and all,
   run from sin and danger!
   Christians come, let nothing grieve you:
        you are freed!
        All you need
   I will surely give to you.'

3 Gather, then, from every nation;
        here let all,
        great and small,
   kneel in adoration;
   love him who with love is yearning:
        Hail the star
        that from far
   bright with hope is burning!

4 You, my Lord, with love I'll cherish,
        live to you,
        and with you
   dying, shall not perish,
   but shall dwell with you for ever:
        joy divine
        shall be mine
   that can alter never.

15
Mo Wilkinson
© Thankyou Music †

1 ·All the way, all the way,
he came all the way for me;
all the way, all the way,
he came all the way for me.

2 From heaven above to Bethlehem
he came all the way for me . . .

3 From Bethlehem to Jerusalem
he came all the way for me . . .

4 From Jerusalem to Calvary
he came all the way for me . . .

5 From Calvary to heaven above
he came all the way for me . . .

6 From heaven above into my heart
he came all the way for me . . .

7 Jesus came, Jesus came,
he came all the way for me . . .

16
© Michael Perry / Jubilate Hymns

1 Alleluia, hear the angels sing,
alleluia through the skies;
alleluia where the infant king
sleeping in a manger lies.

2 Alleluia, let the whole world sing,
alleluia through the earth;
alleluia, joyful carols bring –
come to greet the saviour's birth!

17
Unknown
© Copyright controlled †

Alleluia to the King of kings;
alleluia to the Lamb:
alleluia to the Lord of Lords;
who is the great 'I Am'!

18
Patrick Lee
© Magnificat Music †

Alleluia! Hurry, the Lord is near.
Alleluia, alleluia!
Hurry, the Lord is near.

1 Sound the trumpet, the Lord is near;
Hurry, the Lord is near;
see, he comes to save us all.
hurry, the Lord is near!
Alleluia! Hurry . . .

2 Earth has longed for his approach:
Hurry, the Lord is near;
straighten the road, smooth the path.
hurry, the Lord is near!
Alleluia! Hurry . . .

3 Go out to meet him, shout his name:
Hurry, the Lord is near;
his mighty kingdom shall never end.
hurry, the Lord is near!
Alleluia! Hurry . . .

4 He is the mighty One, he is the Word;
Hurry, the Lord is near;
God everlasting, prince of peace.
hurry, the Lord is near!
Alleluia! Hurry . . .

19
Tim Cullen
© Celebration Services / Thankyou Music †

Alleluia, my Father,
for giving us your Son;
sending him into the world
to be given up for us,
knowing we would bruise him
and smite him from the earth:

Alleluia, my Father –
in his death is my birth;
alleluia, my Father –
in his life is my life!

20
From Isaiah 40

Alleluia, alleluia;
alleluia, alleluia!

Prepare the way for the Lord,
make his path straight:
and all mankind
shall see the salvation of our God.
Alleluia . . .

21
J Montgomery (1771–1854)
© in this version Jubilate Hymns

1 Angels from the realms of glory,
wing your flight through all the earth;
heralds of creation's story
now proclaim Messiah's birth!
Come and worship
Christ, the new-born king:
come and worship,
worship Christ the new-born king.

2 Shepherds in the fields abiding,
watching by your flocks at night,
God with us is now residing:
see, there shines the infant light!
Come and worship . . .

3 Wise men, leave your contemplations!
brighter visions shine afar;
seek in him the hope of nations,
you have seen his natal star:
Come and worship . . .

4 Though an infant now we view him,
he will share his Father's throne,
gather all the nations to him;
every knee shall then bow down:
Come and worship . . .

22
English traditional
© in this version Word & Music / Jubilate Hymns

1 As Joseph was awaking
he heard an angel sing,
'There shall be born to Mary
on earth your heavenly king.'

2 And neither was he born
  in house nor yet in hall,
  but coldly in a stable,
  and in an ox's stall.
    Glory in the highest:
    sing to God 'Nowell'!
    Glory in the highest:
    sing to God, 'Nowell'!

3 And neither was he covered
  in finery or fair,
  but humbly in the clothing
  that all the babies wear.
    Glory . . .

4 And neither was he cradled
  in silver or in gold,
  but softly in a manger
  to keep him from the cold!

23
W C Dix (1837–1898)
© in this version Word & Music / Jubilate Hymns

1 As with gladness men of old
  did the guiding star behold,
  as with joy they hailed its light,
  leading onward, gleaming bright:
  so, most gracious Lord, may we
  evermore your splendour see.

2 As with joyful steps they sped
  to that lowly manger bed,
  there to bend the knee before
  Christ whom heaven and earth adore:
  so with ever-quickening pace
  may we seek your throne of grace.

3 As they offered gifts most rare
  at your cradle plain and bare,
  so may we with holy joy
  pure and free from sin's alloy,
  all our costliest treasures bring,
  Christ, to you, our heavenly king.

4 Holy Jesus, every day
  keep us in the narrow way,
  and when earthly things are past,
  bring our ransomed souls at last:
  where they need no star to guide,
  where no clouds your glory hide.

5 In the heavenly country bright
  none shall need created light –
  Christ, its light, its joy, its crown,
  Christ its sun which goes not down:
  there for ever may we sing
  alleluias to our king.

24
From Revelation 1
Dave Fellingham
© Thankyou Music †

1 At your feet we fall, mighty risen Lord,
  as we come before your throne to worship you!
  By your Spirit's power
      you now draw our hearts,
  and we hear your voice
      in triumph ringing clear:

'I am he that lives,
  that lives and was dead!
  Behold I am alive –
  alive evermore!'

2 There we see you stand, mighty risen Lord,
  clothed in garments pure and holy,
      shining bright;
  eyes of flashing fire, feet like burnished bronze,
  and the sound of many waters is your voice.
    'I am he that lives . . .

3 Like the shining sun in its noon-day strength,
  we now see the glory of your wondrous face:
  once that face was marred,
      but now you're glorified;
  and your words, like a two-edged sword,
      have mighty power.
    'I am he that lives . . .

25/27
verses 1, 2 unknown (nineteenth century)
verse 3 J T McFarland (c.1906)

1 Away in a manger, no crib for a bed,
  the little Lord Jesus laid down his sweet head;
  the stars in the bright sky
      looked down where he lay,
  the little Lord Jesus asleep on the hay.

2 The cattle are lowing, the baby awakes,
  but little Lord Jesus no crying he makes:
  I love you, Lord Jesus – look down from on high
  and stay by my side until morning is nigh.

3 Be near me, Lord Jesus; I ask you to stay
  close by me for ever and love me, I pray;
  bless all the dear children in your tender care,
  and fit us for heaven to live with you there.

26
verses 1, 2 unknown (nineteenth century)
verse 3 J T McFarland (c.1906)

1 SOLO WITH RESPONSE BY ALL
  Away in a manger (away in a manger),
    no crib for a bed (no crib for a bed),
  the little Lord Jesus (the little Lord Jesus)
    laid down his sweet head
      (laid down his sweet head);
  the stars in the bright sky
      (the stars in the bright sky)
    looked down where he lay
      (looked down where he lay),
  the little Lord Jesus (the little Lord Jesus)
    asleep on the hay (asleep on the hay).

2 SOLO
  The cattle are lowing, the baby awakes,
  but little Lord Jesus no crying he makes:
  I love you, Lord Jesus – look down from on high
  and stay by my side until morning is nigh.

3 SOLO WITH RESPONSE BY ALL
  Be near me, Lord Jesus
      (be near me Lord Jesus);
  I ask you to stay I ask you to stay
  close by me for ever (close by me for ever)
    and love me, I pray (and love me, I pray);

bless all the dear children
   (bless all the dear children)
in your tender care (in your tender care),
and fit us for heaven (and fit us for heaven)
to live with you there (to live with you there).

28 Hilda Dodd
© Winifred E Barnard /
Religious and Moral Education Press †

Baby Jesus, sleeping softly
on the warm and fragrant hay,
children all the wide world over
think of you on Christmas Day.

Mother Mary watching Jesus
sleeping in the soft warm hay,
children all the wide world over
think of you on Christmas Day.

Joseph standing close behind them
hearing what the shepherds say,
children all the wide world over
think of you on Christmas Day.

29/30 From Philippians 2 (*The Song of Christ's Glory*)
© Brian Black and Word & Music / Jubilate Hymns

Before the heaven and earth
were made by God's decree,
the Son of God all-glorious dwelt
in God's eternity.

Though in the form of God
and rich beyond compare,
he did not stay to grasp his prize;
nor did he linger there.

From heights of heaven he came
to this world full of sin,
to meet with hunger, hatred, hell,
our life, our love to win.

The Son became true man
and took a servant's role;
with lowliness and selfless love
he came, to make us whole.

Obedient to his death –
that death upon the cross,
no son had ever shown such love,
nor father known such loss.

To him enthroned on high,
by angel hosts adored,
all knees shall bow, and tongues confess
that Jesus Christ is Lord.

31 From 1 Corinthians 15
Phil Rogers
© Thankyou Music †

Behold, I tell you a mystery;
behold, I tell you a mystery!
We shall not all sleep,
but we shall all be changed –
in a moment, in a twinkling of an eye;
in a moment, in a twinkling of an eye.

For the last trumpet shall sound,
and the dead shall be raised incorruptible
and we shall be changed,
we shall be changed.

2 Death is swallowed up in victory;
death is swallowed up in victory!
O death, where is your sting?
The sting of death is sin –
but thanks be to God who gives us victory
through Jesus Christ our Lord!
For the last . . .

32 From Isaiah 60
© in this version Word & Music / Jubilate Hymns

1 Behold the darkness shall cover the earth,
and thick darkness the people;
but the Lord shall arise upon you,
and his glory shall be seen upon you.
So arise, shine for your light is come
and the glory of the Lord is risen;
so arise, shine for your light is come
and the glory of the Lord is upon you!

2 The nations will come to your light,
and kings to the brightness of your dawn;
and they shall call you the city of the Lord,
the Zion of the Holy One of Israel.
So arise . . .

3 Lift up your eyes round about and see –
they gather themselves together:
and they shall come, your sons from afar,
and your daughters shall be nursed
         at your side.
So arise . . .

4 Then you will look and be radiant,
and your heart will throb with joy;
the richness of the sea will be brought to you,
and the nations shall all come to you.
So arise . . .

5 The sun shall not shine by day,
nor shall the moon gleam at night;
but the Lord shall be your everlasting light,
and the days of your mourning shall be ended.
So arise . . .

33 © Michael Perry / Jubilate Hymns

1 Bethlehem, the chosen city of our God,
where the stem of faithful Jesse duly flowered:
there Messiah in a manger humbly lay,
born of Mary, born for us on Christmas Day!

2 Israel's land had suffered much
        in grief and pain
till the hand of God
        should touch the earth again;
then the royal star of Jacob would arise,
David's sceptre soon appear before their eyes.

3 Judah's hills their age-long vigil silent kept,
God fulfilled his pledge while Israel sullen slept;
only shepherds watching bravely
        through the night
found their Shepherd,
        stooped to see the infant light.

4 Bethlehem, the chosen city of our God,
where the stem of faithful Jesse duly flowered:
there Messiah in a manger humbly lay,
born of Mary, born for us on Christmas Day!

34
After B de La Monnoye
© Paul Wigmore / Jubilate Hymns

1 Bethlehem, we come to bring
merry dances for your king!
   Step by step and drum by drum,
pat-a-pat-a-pan, pat-a-pat-a-pan;
step by step and drum by drum
stepping bravely, here we come!

2 Mary, may we come to sing
merry songs to Christ our king?
   Step by step . . .
stepping softly, here we come!

3 Christian people, now we say
merry Christmas on this day!
   Step by step . . .
stepping gladly, here we come!

35
After Prudentius (348–c.413)
© Michael Perry / Jubilate Hymns

1 Bethlehem, what greater city
can in fame with you compare?
For the gracious God of heaven
chose to meet his people there.

2 Was there ever beauty brighter
than the star which shone that night
to proclaim the incarnation
of our God, the world's true light?

3 From the East come men of learning:
rich the treasures that they hold –
tributes to a greater wisdom,
gifts of incense, myrrh and gold.

4 Mighty king their gold proclaims him,
incense shows that God has come;
sacrifice, redeemer, saviour –
myrrh foretells his silent tomb.

5 Jesus Christ, to you be glory,
Lord of lords whom we adore
with the Father and the Spirit:
God be praised for evermore!

36
From Psalm 102
Unknown

Bless the Lord, O my soul,
bless the Lord, O my soul,
and all that is within me
bless his holy name;
bless the Lord . . .
   King of kings (for ever and ever),
   Lord of lords (for ever and ever)
   King of kings (for ever and ever),
   King of kings and Lord of lords!

Bless the Lord . . .

37
From Psalm 95, Joel 2 etc.
© Michael Perry / Jubilate Hymns

1 Blow upon the trumpet!
clap your hands together,
sound aloud the praises of the Lord your king.
He has kept his promise,
granting us salvation:
let his people jubilantly shout and sing!

2 Blow upon the trumpet!
let the nations tremble;
see his power obliterate the sun and moon.
This is God's own army
bringing all to judgement,
for the day of Jesus Christ is coming soon.

3 Blow upon the trumpet!
arrows in the lightning
fly the storm of battle where he marches on.
Glory to our shepherd
keeping us through danger,
setting us like jewels in his royal crown!

4 Blow upon the trumpet!
Christ is surely coming,
heaven's forces mobilizing at his word.
We shall rise to meet him:
death at last is conquered,
God gives us the victory
        through Christ our Lord!

38/39
© Michael Perry / Jubilate Hymns

1 Born as a stranger,
laid in a manger,
   Jesus, the Lord of heaven and earth;
to us descending,
sinners befriending,
   bring us to glory by your birth!

2 Infant so tender!
Gone is the splendour,
   Jesus, that graced your Father's home;
our nature wearing,
our sorrows bearing,
   poor and alone for us you come.

3 Lord of all lowliness,
perfect in holiness,
   Jesus the Christ, of whom we sing;
we bow before you,
praise and adore you:
   be our true saviour and our king!

40
Geoffrey Ainger
© Stainer & Bell Limited †

Born in the night,
  Mary's child,
a long way from your home;
coming in need,
  Mary's child,
born in a borrowed room:

Clear shining light,
  Mary's child,
your face lights up our way:
light of the world,
  Mary's child,
dawn on our darkened day.

Truth of our life,
  Mary's child,
you tell us God is good:
prove it is true,
  Mary's child,
go to your cross of wood.

Hope of the world,
  Mary's child,
you're coming soon to reign:
king of the earth,
  Mary's child,
walk in our streets again,
walk in our streets again.

41
R Heber (1783–1826)
© in this version Jubilate Hymns

Brightest and best of the suns of the morning,
dawn on our darkness and come to our aid;
star of the east, the horizon adorning,
guide where our infant redeemer is laid!

What shall we give him, in costly devotion?
Shall we bring incense and offerings divine,
gems of the mountain and pearls of the ocean,
myrrh from the forest or gold from the mine?

Vainly we offer each lavish oblation,
vainly with gifts would his favour secure;
richer by far is the heart's adoration,
dearer to God are the prayers of the poor.

Brightest and best of the suns of the morning,
dawn on our darkness and come to our aid;
star of the east, the horizon adorning,
guide where our infant redeemer is laid!

42
After M MacDonald (1789–1872)
L Macbean (1853–1931)

Child in the manger, infant of Mary,
outcast and stranger, Lord of all!
child who inherits all our transgressions,
all our demerits on him fall.

Once the most holy child of salvation
gentle and lowly lived below:
now as our glorious mighty redeemer,
see him victorious over each foe.

3 Prophets foretold him, infant of wonder;
angels behold him on his throne:
worthy our saviour of all their praises;
happy for ever are his own.

43
After E Fléchier (1632–1710)
© Michael Perry / Jubilate Hymns

1 Child in a stable:
how lovely is this place
  where God is able
to show such perfect grace!
No princely babe that smiled
or palace that beguiled,
in history or fable,
could ever match this child
  within a stable.

2 God comes in weakness,
and to our world for love
  descends with meekness
from realms of light above.
This Child shall heal our wrong,
for sorrow give a song,
and hope in place of bleakness;
for nothing is so strong
  as God in weakness.

3 Now night is ended!
the chasm that divides
  at last is mended,
and God with us abides.
For on this happy morn
new glory wakes the dawn;
the Sun is high ascended –
to us a Child is born,
  and night is ended!

44/45   © Michael Perry / Jubilate Hymns

1 Child of gladness, child of sorrow,
crib today and cross tomorrow;
holy child who comes to borrow
  peasant robe and stable bare:

2 Child as all our children tender,
prince removed from heaven's splendour:
wealth and glory you surrender
  all our bitter pain to share.

3 Child in Bethlehem appearing,
neither hurt nor hatred fearing:
you we worship, God revering,
  Jesus, saviour, hear our prayer.

46
J M Neale (1818–1866)
© in this version Word & Music / Jubilate Hymns

1 Christ is born for us today –
rough the manger, soft the hay;
all who will confess him may
receive the Son, the holy One of Mary.

2 Child of grace at Mary's knee,
he is born to set us free;
he is born our hope to be,
our God, our Lord, by all adored for ever.

3 Christians all, rejoice and sing
with the coming of our King;
let the bells of heaven ring
to tell the earth of Jesus' birth to Mary!

47

1 Christ is born to be our king –
listen, as the angels sing,
to the heavens echoing,
'Glory be to God on high!'

2 Shepherds in the fields at night
hear the tidings, see the light,
find the child, in praise unite:
'Glory be to God on high!'

3 Christians down the ages tell
Christ can break the powers of hell,
so that we may sing as well,
'Glory be to God on high!'

48

1 Christ is born within a stable:
greet the day when heaven smiled!
Shepherds, fast as they are able,
run to see the holy Child.
Alleluia, alleluia,
alleluia! Amen.

2 Eastern skies are brightly shining,
hope has come upon the earth;
angel songs with ours combining
tell the world of Jesus' birth.
Alleluia . . .

3 Peal the bells and set them ringing,
spread the joyful news abroad;
come with faith and join our singing
to acclaim the incarnate Lord!
Alleluia . . .

49

1 Christ is surely coming bringing his reward,
omega and alpha, first and last and Lord;
root and stem of David, brilliant morning star –
Meet your judge and saviour,
nations near and far;
meet your judge and saviour,
nations near and far!

2 See the holy city! There they enter in,
all by Christ made holy, washed from every sin;
thirsty ones, desiring all he loves to give:
Come for living water,
freely drink, and live;
come for living water,
freely drink, and live!

3 Grace be with God's people!
Praise his holy name –
Father, Son and Spirit, evermore the same!
Hear the certain promise
from the eternal home:
'Surely I come quickly!' –
Come, Lord Jesus, come;
'Surely I come quickly!' –
Come, Lord Jesus, come!

50

1 Christ was born on Christmas day,
Sing, sing, for Christ is born;
lowly in his manger lay,
all on that Christmas morn.
Alleluia, alleluia,
alleluia, Christ is born;
alleluia, alleluia,
all on that Christmas morn.

2 The shepherds heard the angels sing,
Sing, sing, for Christ is born,
went to the stable and found their king
all on that Christmas morn.
Alleluia . . .

3 The wise men followed when they saw the star
Sing, sing, for Christ is born,
bringing him presents from afar,
all on that Christmas morn.
Alleluia . . .

4 So let us now sing songs of praise,
Sing, sing, for Christ is born,
and to him alleluias raise,
all on that Christmas morn:
Alleluia . . .

51

1 Christians, awake, salute the happy morn
on which the saviour of the world was born;
rise to adore the mystery of love
which hosts of angels chanted from above!
With them the joyful tidings first began
of Mary's infant and our God made man.

2 Then to the watchful shepherds it was told,
who heard the herald angel's voice: 'Behold,
I bring good tidings of a holy birth
to you and every nation on the earth:
this day has God fulfilled the promised word,
this day is born a saviour, Christ the Lord!

3 To Bethlehem these shepherds swiftly run
to see the wonder of God's only Son;
they find with Joseph and the lowly maid,
the new-born saviour in a manger laid.
In human form their Shepherd they discern,
and to their flocks, still praising God, return.

O may we keep and ponder in our mind
God's gracious love in saving lost mankind:
trace we his footsteps who retrieved our loss,
from his poor manger to his bitter cross.
Saved by his love, unceasing we shall sing
eternal praise to heaven's mighty king!

5 Infant lowly, born in squalor,
  prophet, king and great high priest,
  Word of God, to us descending:
  still we sing, both great and least,
    to our God . . .

52

From the Latin (c.1500)
© Michael Perry / Jubilate Hymns

Christians, make a joyful sound,
sing to all the world around:
he is in a manger found,
the holy One, the infant son of Mary.
  Let the people join and say
  that Christ the Lord is born today,
  till the very earth shall raise
  the song of praise:
  'Nowell, nowell –
  Christ is born, the infant son of Mary!'

Mighty God, Emmanuel –
prince of whom the prophets tell,
child announced by Gabriel,
the holy One, the infant son of Mary.
  Let the people . . .

Come, you choirs, with gladness sing,
instruments of music bring –
eager to proclaim the king,
the holy One, the infant son of Mary.
  Let the people . . .

Love is here to seek and save –
heaven's master as a slave:
God so loved the world he gave
the holy One, the infant son of Mary.
  Let the people . . .

53

© Michael Saward / Jubilate Hymns

Christmas for God's holy people
is a time of joy and peace:
so, all Christian men and women,
hymns and carols let us raise
  to our God
  come to earth,
Son of Man, by human birth.

Child of Mary, virgin mother,
peasant baby, yet our king,
cradled there among the oxen:
joyful carols now we sing
  to our God . . .

Angel armies sang in chorus
at our Christ's nativity;
he who came to share our nature:
so we sing with gaiety
  to our God . . .

Shepherds hurried to the manger,
saw the babe in Bethlehem,
glorified the God of heaven:
now we join to sing with them
  to our God . . .

54

© David Mowbray / Jubilate Hymns

1 Christmas news! Christ is born,
  night has fled – bright the dawn,
  angel hosts greet the morn,
  shepherds there adore him,
  wise men kneel before him.
    Lift your hearts today –
    mercy starts today.
    Christmas news!
    Christ is born,
    Christ our Lord and Saviour.

2 Christmas news! Christ the boy –
  Israel's hope, Mary's joy –
  Herod's hate can't destroy:
  now he takes our nature,
  grows in grace and stature.
    Lift your hearts today . . .

3 Christmas news! Christ stoops low,
  all our grief he will know,
  every hurt, every blow,
  like his human brothers –
  yet unlike all others.
    Lift your hearts today . . .

4 Christmas news! Christ the Lord
  in our world has restored
  what was spoilt, what was flawed:
  praise his incarnation,
  cross and resurrection.
    Lift your hearts today . . .

55

From Psalm 47
Herbert Chappell
© Chappell Music Ltd / International Music Publications †

SOLO
Clap your hands, clap your hands;
shout to God with the voice of triumph.

ALL
Clap your hands, clap your hands;
shout to God with the voice of triumph.

SOLO
For the Lord most high is powerful.
He's the king of all the earth.

ALL
For the Lord most high is powerful.
He's the king of all the earth.

SOLO
He'll subdue the people under us,
and the nations under our feet.

ALL
He'll subdue the people under us,
and the nations under our feet.

God is gone up with a shout,
and the Lord with sounds of trumpets.

ALL
God is gone up with a shout,
and the Lord with sounds of trumpets.

SOLO
Clap your hands, clap your hands,
shout to God with the voice of triumph.
(Optional repeat from *)

ALL
Clap your hands, clap your hands,
shout to God with the voice of triumph.

SOLO
O clap your hands.

ALL
O clap your hands.

56 From Psalm 47
© Judy Davies / Jubilate Hymns

Clap your hands, you people;
shout to God with a voice of triumph!
Sing to God, sing praises,
for he is highly exalted!

1 For the Lord most high is mighty,
he is king in all the earth;
he subdues the far-flung nations,
he ordains our time and birth.
Clap your hands . . .

2 God in majesty is reigning:
praise the Lord with shout and song!
Praise his name with psalm and trumpet;
praise him, all you princely throng!
Clap your hands . . .

3 Kings and nobles, pay him homage,
bow before his holy throne:
his the power throughout creation;
he is Lord, and he alone!
Clap your hands . . .

57 From Psalm 93
© Michael Saward / Jubilate Hymns

1 Clothed in kingly majesty,
robed in regal power,
God is over all.

2 Lord of all, unshakeable,
throned beyond all time,
God is over all.

3 Greater than the river's roar
and the surging sea,
God is over all.

4 Changeless as his law's decrees,
crowned our holy king,
God is over all.

58 © Michael Saward / Jubilate Hymns

1 Come all you good people and burst into song!
be joyful and happy, your praises prolong;
remember the birthday of Jesus our king,
who brings us salvation: his glory we sing.

2 His mother, a virgin so gentle and pure,
was told of God's promise,
unchanging and sure,
foretelling the birthday of Jesus our king,
who brings us salvation: his glory we sing.

3 To Bethlehem hurried the shepherds amazed,
with stories of angels and heavens that blazed
proclaiming the birthday of Jesus our king,
who brings us salvation: his glory we sing.

4 So come let us honour the babe in the hay
and give him our homage and worship today,
recalling the birthday of Jesus our king,
who brings us salvation: his glory we sing.

59 © Michael Perry / Jubilate Hymns

1 Come and hear the joyful singing,
Alleluia, gloria,
set the bells of heaven ringing:
alleluia, gloria,
God the Lord has shown us favour –
alleluia, gloria,
Christ is born to be our saviour.
Alleluia, gloria!

2 Angels of his birth are telling,
Alleluia, gloria,
prince of peace all powers excelling;
alleluia, gloria,
death and hell can not defeat him:
alleluia, gloria,
go to Bethlehem and greet him.
Alleluia, gloria!

3 Choir and people, shout in wonder,
Alleluia, gloria,
let the merry organ thunder;
alleluia, gloria,
thank our God for love amazing,
alleluia, gloria,
Father, Son and Spirit praising.
Alleluia, gloria!

60 From Luke 2
© Michael Perry / Jubilate Hymns

1 Come and hear the news,
the news of Christmas joy for all people!

2 'Go today, find your redeemer:
he is born in Bethlehem!'

3 Angels sing, good news they bring,
joyful news of the saviour:
go to Bethlehem and find him
lying in a manger – Christ the Lord!
Listen . . .

Let's go to Bethlehem and find him;
the saviour prophets have foretold.
He is lying in a manger –
Christ the saviour who is born for us:
let's . . .

Praises sing to our King –
praise to the Prince of peace.
Let us praises sing to our King –
for his name is Wonderful Counsellor,
so . . .

'Glory in the highest heaven;
peace on earth, good will to all!'

61

Valerie Collison
© High-Fye Music Ltd. †

Come and join the celebration –
it's a very special day;
come and share our jubilation –
there's a new king born today!

See the shepherds hurry down to Bethlehem,
gaze in wonder at the Son of God
who lies before them:
Come and join . . .

Wise men journey, led to worship by a star,
kneel in homage, bringing precious gifts
from lands afar, so
Come and join . . .

'God is with us!' –
round the world the message bring;
he is with us – 'Welcome!'
all the bells on earth are pealing:
Come and join . . .

62

From Revelation 4–5
© Christopher Idle / Jubilate Hymns

Come and see the shining hope
that Christ's apostle saw;
on the earth, confusion,
but in heaven an open door,
where the living creatures
praise the Lamb for evermore:
Love has the victory for ever!
Amen, he comes! to bring his own reward!
Amen, praise God! for justice now restored;
kingdoms of the world become
the kingdoms of the Lord:
Love has the victory for ever!

All the gifts you send us, Lord,
are faithful, good, and true;
holiness and righteousness
are shown in all you do:
who can see your greatest Gift
and fail to worship you?
Love has the victory for ever!
Amen, he comes . . .

3 Power and salvation all belong to God on high!
So the mighty multitudes of heaven
make their cry,
singing Alleluia! where the echoes never die:
Love has the victory for ever!
Amen, he comes . . .

63

© Michael Perry / Jubilate Hymns

1 Come and sing the Christmas story
this holy night!
Christ is born: the hope of glory
dawns on our sight.
Alleluia! earth is ringing
with a thousand angels singing –
hear the message they are bringing
this holy night.

2 Jesus, Saviour, child of Mary
this holy night,
in a world confused and weary
you are our light.
God is in a manger lying,
manhood taking, self denying,
life embracing, death defying
this holy night.

3 Lord of all! Let us acclaim him
this holy night;
king of our salvation name him,
throned in the height.
Son of Man – let us adore him:
all the earth is waiting for him;
Son of God – we bow before him
this holy night.

64

© Michael Perry / Jubilate Hymns

1 Come and praise the Lord our king, Alleluia,
let the world with carols ring. alleluia!

2 Hear the news the angels tell, Alleluia,
Christ is born, and all is well. alleluia!

3 With the shepherds make your way, Alleluia,
find the Son of God today. alleluia!

4 See the gifts the wise men hold – Alleluia,
they bring incense, myrrh and gold. alleluia!

5 In our praises take your part, Alleluia,
thank him with a joyful heart. alleluia!

6 Come and praise the Lord our king, Alleluia,
let the world with carols ring. alleluia!

65

From Psalm 86
Rose Smith
© Thankyou Music †

Come, let us glorify the Lord,
sing Alleluia to the Lord;
come, let us worship him,
bow down and worship him,
for he is God and Lord of all!

66
Pat Ogle
© Thankyou Music †

1 Come, let us kneel before him,
come, let us praise his name;
worship the Lord our God:

2 For he has borne our sorrows,
and he has borne our griefs,
that we might walk redeemed.

3 Wake, all who live in Zion;
sing, all you war-torn lands:
the Prince of peace is come!

67
© Norman Warren / Jubilate Hymns

1 Come, Lord Jesus, come Lord Jesus;
come and make our hearts your home!
We bow before you, we love and adore you,
acknowledge that you are Lord of all:
Come, Lord Jesus, come Lord Jesus;
come and make our hearts your home.

2 Come, Lord Jesus, come Lord Jesus;
come and make this world your own!
We bow before you, we love and adore you,
acknowledge that you are Lord of all:
Come, Lord Jesus, come, Lord Jesus;
come and make this world your own.

68
From Psalm 95
Sarah Turner-Smith
© Ears and Eyes Music †

Come, let us worship our redeemer,
let us bow down before his throne;
come, let us kneel before our maker –
holy is his name.

1 Come into his presence with thanksgiving,
make a joyful noise
for the Lord is a great God –
king above all Gods.

2 We are the people of his pasture,
the sheep of his hand,
for Christ the Lord is our shepherd,
he will lead us home.
Come, let us ...

3 All praises be to God the Father,
praise to Christ his Son;
praise be to God the Holy Spirit:
bless the Three-in-One!
Come, let us ...

Holy is his name!

69
From Psalm 95
David Williams
© Thankyou Music †

Come on, let us sing to the Lord,
come on, let us worship the king;
come on, let us shout aloud
and come before him with thanksgiving.

1 We will extol him
with music and with song,
we will bow before him;
the Lord he is our God.
Come on ...

2 Let us kneel before our God
in praise and adoration:
he is the king of kings,
he is the lord of Lords.
Come on ...

70
C Wesley (1707–1788)
© in this version Jubilate Hymns

1 Come, O long-expected Jesus,
born to set your people free!
from our fears and sins release us,
Christ in whom our rest shall be.

2 Israel's strength and consolation,
born salvation to impart;
dear desire of every nation,
joy of every longing heart:

3 Born your people to deliver,
born a child and yet a king;
born to reign in us for ever,
now your gracious kingdom bring:

4 By your own eternal Spirit
rule in all our hearts alone;
by your all-sufficient merit
raise us to your glorious throne.

71
© David Mowbray / Jubilate Hymns

1 Come ride with kings to Bethlehem
and kneel in company with them;
follow the shepherds with delight
and find the child they found that night.
God so loved the world, he gave
his Son mankind to save.

2 Come join the angels gathering
and listen to the songs they sing;
help spread the news for all to hear
of Christ beneath the shining star.
God so loved ...

3 Let Mary's wonder overflow
that all God's promises are true;
come see by her humanity
God's presence and divinity.
God so loved ...

4 Then celebrate, come dance and sing!
This child is here God's peace to bring;
his truth and joy for all to grant,
his kingdom in our lives to plant.
God so loved ...

72

1 Come now with awe,
    earth's ancient vigil keeping:
cold under starlight lies the stony way.
Down from the hillside
    see the shepherds creeping,
hear in our hearts
    the whispered news they say:
'Laid in a manger lies an infant sleeping,
Christ our Redeemer, born for us today.'

2 Come now with joy to worship and adore him;
hushed in the stillness, wonder and behold –
Christ in the stable where his mother bore him,
Christ whom the prophets faithfully foretold:
    High King of ages, low we kneel before him,
    starlight for silver, lantern-light for gold.

3 Come now with faith,
    the age-long secret guessing,
hearts rapt in wonder, soul and spirit stirred –
see in our likeness love beyond expressing,
all God has spoken, all the prophets heard;
    born for us sinners, bearer of all blessing,
    flesh of our flesh, behold the eternal Word!

4 Come now with love:
    beyond our comprehending
love in its fulness lies in mortal span!
How should we love,
    whom Love is so befriending?
Love rich in mercy since our race began
    now stoops to save us,
    sighs and sorrows ending,
Jesus our Saviour, Son of God made man.

73

1 Cradle rocking, cattle lowing,
bright star guiding men to see
little Christ-child in the manger,
light of all the world to be:
    Alleluia, holy Child,
    hosanna in the highest;
    gloria, Emmanuel,
    hosanna in the highest!

2 Mother Mary, watching carefully
by the light of one bright star;
Bread of heaven, softly sleeping,
gentle gift of God to man:
    Alleluia . . .

3 Who could guess, to see you lie there,
that you came to bring a sword?
Prince of peace, born in a manger,
with a price upon your soul.
    Alleluia . . .

4 Do you know – so weak and helpless –
of the grace you bear to us;
do you dream yet of the kingdom
you will some day bring to pass?
    Alleluia . . .

74

Come to set us free,
come to make us your own;
come to show the way to your people,
    your chosen:
open our lives to the light of your promise.
Come to our hearts with healing,
come to our minds with power;
come to us and bring us your life.

1 You are light which shines in darkness,
Morning Star which never sets:
open our eyes which only dimly see
the truth which sets us free.
    Come to set us free . . .

2 You are hope which brings us courage,
you are strength which never fails:
open our minds to ways we do not know,
but where your Spirit grows.
    Come to set us free . . .

3 You are promise of salvation,
you are God in human form:
bring to our world of emptiness and fear
the word we long to hear.
    Come to set us free . . .

75

1 Down from the height of his glory he came,
willingly leaving his rightful domain:
Jesus was born in the image of man,
love was his motive and mercy his aim.

2 All through those days
    his resolve was the same –
Jesus the servant, the sharer of pain:
perfect obedience, the path of disdain,
down to a death of derision and shame.

3 Now God has granted him honour and fame,
taken him up to the highest to reign:
'Jesus is Lord.' every voice shall maintain,
all of creation shall bow to his name.

76

1 Darkness like a shroud
covers the earth,
evil like a cloud
covers the people;
but the Lord will rise upon you,
and his glory will appear on you,
nations will come to your light.
    Arise, shine, your light has come,
    the glory of the Lord has risen on you;
    arise, shine, your light has come –
    Jesus the light of the world has come.

2 Children of the light,
be clean and pure;
rise, you sleepers,
Christ will shine on you:
take the Spirit's flashing two-edged sword
and with faith declare God's mighty word;
stand up, and in his strength be strong!
    Arise, shine, your light has come,
    the glory of the Lord has risen on you;
    arise, shine, your light has come –
    Jesus the light of the world has come.

3 Here among us now,
Christ the Light
kindles brighter flames
in our trembling hearts:
Living Word, our lamp, come guide our feet –
as we walk as one in light and peace,
justice and truth shine like the sun.
    Arise, shine . . .

4 Like a city bright,
so let us blaze;
lights in every street
turning night to day:
and the darkness shall not overcome,
till the fullness of Christ's kingdom comes,
dawning to God's eternal day.
    Arise, shine . . .

Jesus the light of the world,
Jesus the light of the world,
Jesus the light of the world has come.

77 G R Woodward (1848–1934)

1 Ding dong! Merrily on high
    in heaven the bells are ringing.
Ding dong! Verily the sky
    is riven with angels singing:
        Gloria, hosanna in excelsis;
        gloria, hosanna in excelsis!

2 E'en so, here below, below,
    let steeple bells be swungen;
and i-o, i-o, i-o,
    by priest and people sungen!
        Gloria . . .

3 Pray you, dutifully prime
    your matin chime, you ringers;
may you beautifully rhyme
    your evetime song, you singers:
        Gloria . . .

78 Unknown
© Copyright controlled †

Ding, dong, ring out the carillon;
ding, dong, joy is here:
ding, dong, let every care be gone;
ding, dong, Christmas cheer!

1 In a manger see him lying –
little babe so weak and small:
on his mother's care relying
cradled in a cattle stall.
    Ding, dong . . .

2 See the star so clearly shining,
in the darkness of the night;
wise men of the east it's guiding,
by its radiance led aright.
    Ding, dong . . .

3 Here the angel voices singing,
'Peace on earth, good will to men!'
All the bells of heaven are ringing,
echoing to earth again.
    Ding, dong . . .

79 Dave Fellingham
© Thankyou Music †

Emmanuel, God is with us,
Emmanuel, God is with us.
The Lord of hosts – he is with us,
the God of Jacob is our stronghold,
the Lord most high is our refuge and strength:
God is with us, God is with us
dwelling in the midst of his people.
God is with us, God is with us,
making glad the city of God
as the river of life flows from the throne,
bringing life and strength to all.
We shall not be moved –
God is with us.
    Emmanuel, God with us.
God is now with us.

80 From Isaiah 9 and 53
Graham Kendrick
© Thankyou Music †

Emmanuel – God is with us,
Emmanuel – he is here;
Emmanuel – he is among us;
Emmanuel – his kingdom is here.

1 Wonderful Counsellor,
        they laughed at his wisdom,
the Mighty God on a dusty road;
Everlasting Father, a friend of sinners,
a Prince of peace in a cattle stall.

2 He was despised and rejected,
a man of sorrows acquainted with grief:
from him we turned and hid our faces;
he was despised, him we did not esteem.
    Emmanuel . . .

3 But he was wounded for our transgressions,
he was bruised for our iniquities:
on him was the punishment
        that made us whole,
and by his stripes we are healed.

4 He was oppressed, he was afflicted,
and yet he opened not his mouth:
like a lamb that is led to the slaughter,
like a sheep before his shearers
        he did not speak.
    Emmanuel . . .

81
From Isaiah 7
Bob McGee
© Christian Arts Music / Word Music (UK) †

Emmanuel, Emmanuel,
his name is called Emmanuel –
God with us,
revealed in us –
his name is called Emmanuel.

82
From Philippians 2 (*The Song of Christ's Glory*)
© Gavin Reid

1 Empty he came
as a man to our race,
equal with God
yet forsaking his place –
humbly he served in our world,
humbly he served in our world.

2 Lowlier still,
he was willing to die
nailed to a cross
as the people passed by –
bravely he died in our world,
bravely he died in our world.

3 Raised by our God
for us all to revere,
given a name
that shall stand without peer –
honoured as Lord in our world,
honoured as Lord in our world.

4 Give us that mind
that refuses to claim
even our rights,
make our outlook the same –
humbly to serve in our world,
humbly to serve in our world.

83
From Luke 2 (*The Song of Simeon / Nunc dimittis*)
© Timothy Dudley-Smith †

1 Faithful vigil ended,
watching, waiting cease:
Master, grant your servant
his discharge in peace.

2 All the Spirit promised,
all the Father willed,
now these eyes behold it
perfectly fulfilled.

3 This your great deliverance
sets your people free;
Christ their light uplifted
all the nations see.

4 Christ, your people's glory!
watching, doubting cease:
grant to us your servants
our discharge in peace.

84
Geoff Baker
© Word Music (UK) †

1 Father God, we worship you,
evermore the same:
may the things we say and do,
glorify your name;
from the shelter of your love
let our praises ring,
lifting up the name we love –
children of the King.

2 Jesus, Lord, we worship you,
evermore the same:
may the things we say and do,
glorify your name;
make us daily more like you,
till your face we see,
and in heaven with you we'll reign,
for eternity.

85
From Luke 2
© Michael Perry / Jubilate Hymns

1 'Fear not, for I bring all people
good news of joy, good news of joy,
good news of joy:

2 'On this day in David's city
Jesus is born, Jesus is born,
Jesus is born.

3 'Glory in the highest heaven,
peace on the earth, peace on the earth,
peace on the earth!'

86
From Psalm 24
© Michael Perry / Jubilate Hymns

Fling wide the gates,
unbar the ancient doors;
salute your king
in his triumphant cause!

1 Now all the world belongs to Christ our Lord:
let all creation greet the living Word!
Fling wide . . .

2 Who has the right to worship him today?
All those who gladly serve him and obey.
Fling wide . . .

3 He comes to save all those who trust his name,
and will declare them
free from guilt and shame.
Fling wide . . .

4 Who is the victor glorious from the fight?
He is our king, our life, our Lord, our right!
Fling wide . . .

87
After M Luther (1483–1546)
© Michael Perry / Jubilate Hymns

1 'From heaven above I come to bring
the joyful news of Christ your king:
the holy infant born tonight
shall be your hope and your delight.

2 'For know that God has kept his word
and sends to you this mighty Lord
to free you from your sin and shame;
the saviour, Jesus, is his name.

3 'The One by whom the world was made
is in a humble manger laid;
and he to whom the throne was given
now stoops to raise you up to heaven.'

4 So with the shepherds make your way,
and find in Bethlehem today
the child of peace, the ever-blessed,
your master and your gracious guest.

5 Then bear the news that angels tell
to all the weary world as well;
let human power and pomp and pride
be vanquished at this Christmastide.

6 Sing praises to the Father, Son,
and Holy Spirit – Three in One;
let God made known in Christ our Lord
be worshipped, honoured, and adored.

88 Graham Kendrick
© Thankyou Music †

1 For this purpose Christ was revealed,
to destroy all the works of the evil one;
Christ in us has overcome,
so with gladness we sing
and welcome his kingdom in.
MEN
Over sin he has conquered:
WOMEN
Alleluia! he has conquered.
MEN
Over death victorious:
WOMEN
Alleluia! victorious.
MEN
Over sickness he has triumphed:
WOMEN
Alleluia! he has triumphed.
ALL
Jesus reigns over all!

2 In the name of Jesus we stand;
by the power of his blood
we now claim this ground:
Satan has no authority here,
powers of darkness must flee,
for Christ has the victory.
MEN
Over sin . . .

89 From Isaiah 9
David J Hadden
© Restoration Music Ltd †

1 For unto us a child is born,
unto us a son is given,
and the government shall be upon his shoulder;
for unto us a child is born,
unto us a son is given,
and the government shall be upon his shoulder.
And he will be called Wonderful,
Wonderful Counsellor, Mighty God,
the Everlasting Father, Prince of peace,
Mighty God.

2 And there shall be no end
to the increase of his rule,
to the increase of his government and peace;
for he shall sit on David's throne
upholding righteousness,
our God shall accomplish this.
And he will be called . . .

3 For he is the Mighty God,
he is the Prince of peace,
the King of kings and Lord of lords:
all honour to the king,
all glory to his name,
for now and for evermore!
And he will be called . . .

90 After Sedulius (died c.450)
and J Ellerton (1826–1893)
© in this version Word & Music / Jubilate Hymns

1 From east to west, from shore to shore,
let earth awake and sing:
the holy child that Mary bore
is Christ, the Lord and King!

2 He did not spurn the ox's stall,
nor scorn the manger bed;
there God whose mercy feeds us all,
by Mary's love was fed.

3 For us the world's Creator wears
the fashion of a slave;
our human flesh the Maker shares,
his creature, comes to save.

4 To shepherds poor, their Lord most high –
their Shepherd – was revealed,
while angel choirs sang in the sky
across the silent field:

5 All glory be to God above,
and on the earth be peace
to all who long to taste his love,
till time itself shall cease!

91 Graham Kendrick
© Thankyou Music †

1 From heaven you came, helpless Babe –
entered our world your glory veiled,
not to be served but to serve,
and give your life that we might live.
This is our God – the servant king,
he calls us now to follow him,
to bring our lives as a daily offering
of worship to the servant king.

2 There in the garden of tears
my heavy load he chose to bear;
his heart with sorrow was torn,
'Yet not my will but yours,' he said.
This is our God . . .

3 Come see his hands and his feet,
the scars that speak of sacrifice,
hands that flung stars into space
to cruel nails surrendered.
This is our God . . .

4 So let us learn how to serve
  and in our lives enthrone him,
  each other's needs to prefer –
  for it is Christ we are serving.
    This is our God . . .

92
C R Vaughan
© Bible Society †

1 From the distant east and the farthest west,
    I will bring my people home:
  let my people return from the distant lands –
    I will bring my people home.
  Someone is shouting in the desert:
  Prepare a road for the Lord,
  make a path straight for him to travel,
  prepare a road for the Lord,
  turn away from your sins!

2 Do not cling to the past or the long ago –
    I will bring my people home:
  I will make a road and the river flow,
    I will bring my people home.
  Someone is shouting . . .

3 Do not be afraid – through the waters deep
    I will bring my people home:
  do not be afraid as you pass through fire –
    I will bring my people home.
  Someone is shouting . . .

    Turn away from your sins,
    turn away from your sins!

93
© Timothy Dudley-Smith †

1 From the Father's throne on high
  Christ returns to rule and reign.
  Child of earth, he came to die;
  Judge of all he comes again.

2 Darkened be the day at noon
  when the stars of heaven fall:
  earth and sky and sun and moon –
  cloudy darkness covers all.

3 Ancient powers of sin and death
  shake to hear the trumpet blown;
  from the winds' remotest breath
  God will gather in his own.

4 So behold the promised sign,
  sky and sea by tumult riven,
  and the King of kings divine
  coming in the clouds of heaven.

5 Come then, Lord, in light and power,
  at whose word the worlds began;
  in the unexpected hour
  come in glory, Son of Man.

94
M Sargent (1895–1967)
© Oxford University Press †
and in this version Word & Music / Jubilate Hymns

1 Girls and boys, leave your toys, make no noise,
  kneel at his crib and worship him.
  For this shrine, Child divine, is the sign
  our Saviour's here.
    Alleluia, the church bells ring,
    'Alleluia!' the angels sing,
    alleluia from everything –
    all must draw near!

2 On that day, far away, Jesus lay –
  angels were watching round his head
  Holy Child, mother mild, undefiled,
  we sing your praise.
    Alleluia . . .
    our hearts we raise.

3 Shepherds came at the fame of your name,
  angels their guide to Bethlehem;
  in that place, saw your face filled with grace,
  stood at your door.
    Alleluia . . .
    love evermore.

95/96
© Michael Perry / Jubilate Hymns

1 Glad music fills the Christmas sky –
  a hymn of praise, a song of love;
  the angels worship high above
  and Mary sings her lullaby.

2 Of tender love for God she sings,
  the chosen mother of the Son;
  she knows that wonders have begun,
  and trusts for all the future brings.

3 The angel chorus of the skies
  who come to tell us of God's grace
  have yet to know his human face,
  to watch him die, to see him rise.

4 Let praise be true and love sincere,
  rejoice to greet the saviour's birth;
  let peace and honour fill the earth
  and mercy reign – for God is here!

5 Then lift your hearts and voices high,
  sing once again the Christmas song:
  for love and praise to Christ belong –
  in shouts of joy, and lullaby.

97
© Lesley Neal †

Glory, glory,
glory to God and peace on earth –
Christ the saviour is born!

Glory, glory,
glory to God and peace on earth –
Christ the Lord and saviour is born today!

98
Tom McLain
© Glory Alleluia Music /
Tempo Music Publications Inc †

Glory, glory, glory to the King,
glory, glory, glory to the King!
Glory . . .

Who is the king of glory?
King Jesus is his name;
he is high and lifted up above the earth,
and his name I will proclaim:
  Glory . . .

99

© Michael Perry / Jubilate Hymns

1 'Glory in the highest heaven,
grace and peace on earth!'
to our world a Son is given,
songs attend his birth:
come with angel hosts to name him,
then proclaim him – tell his worth!

2 Shepherds, these glad tidings hearing,
leave their flock and fold,
seek the place of Christ's appearing –
David's town of old:
come and hasten to adore him,
kneel before him and behold!

3 Wise men travel with their treasure,
frankincense they bring,
gold and myrrh in royal measure –
this their offering:
come in homage, drawing near to him
to revere him – mighty king!

4 Christ is born! the sure salvation
for a world of wrong,
hope of every generation,
truth awaited long:
come with joyful faith to meet him,
gladly greet him with a song!

100

© in this version Richard Bewes /
Jubilate Hymns

Go, tell it on the mountain,
over the hills and everywhere;
go tell it on the mountain,
that Jesus Christ is born!

1 The shepherds from the hillside
gave worship and adored;
they saw the Babe of Bethlehem
was Jesus Christ the Lord:
Go, tell . . .

2 The men from eastern countries
came later there to bring
their gifts of loving homage
to Jesus Christ the King:
Go, tell . . .

3 A road that Jews and Gentiles,
both rich and poor have trod –
it led them all to Bethl'em,
to Christ, the Son of God:
Go, tell . . .

4 The learnèd and the simple
come to the manger-stall;
he joins us in his family,
the saviour of us all!
Go, tell . . .

-101

Marilyn Baker
© Word Music (UK) †

1 God came among us, he became a man,
became a baby,
though through him the world began.
He came to earth to bring us peace,
but where is that peace today?
It can be found
by those who will let him direct their way.

2 He came to serve,
to show us how much he cared;
our joys and sorrows he so willingly shared.
He came to earth to bring us joy,
but where is that joy today?
It can be found
by those who let him wash their guilt away.

3 Death tried to hold him, but it could not succeed;
he rose again, and now we can be freed.
He longs to give eternal life
to all who will simply receive,
yes to all who will open their hearts
and just believe.

102

Austin Martin
© Thankyou Music †

God has exalted him
to the highest place,
given him the name
that is above every name.

And every knee shall bow
and every tongue confess
that Jesus Christ is Lord
to the glory of God the Father.
God has exalted him . . .

103

© Willard Jabusch †

God has spoken to his people
Alleluia,
and his words are words of wisdom.
alleluia!

1 Open your ears, O Christian people,
open your ears and hear good news;
open your hearts, O royal priesthood,
God has come to you, God has come to you.
God has spoken . . .

2 They who have ears to hear his message,
they who have ears, then let them hear;
they who would learn the way of wisdom,
let them hear God's word,
let them hear God's word!
God has spoken . . .

3 Israel comes to greet the saviour,
Judah is glad to see his day;
from east and west the peoples travel,
he will show the way, he will show the way.
God has spoken . . .

104
© Dave Fellingham / Thankyou Music †

God of glory, we exalt your name,
you who reign in majesty;
we lift our hearts to you
and we will worship, praise and magnify
your holy name.

In power resplendent
you reign in glory;
eternal King, you reign for ever:
your word is mighty,
releasing captives,
your love is gracious –
you are my God.

105
After Prudentius (348–c.413)
J M Neale (1818–1866) and H W Baker (1821–1877)
© in this version Jubilate Hymns

1 God of God, the uncreated
love, before the world began;
Christ the source and Christ the ending,
Son of God and Son of Man,
Lord of all the things that have been,
master of the eternal plan,
evermore and evermore.

2 He is here, whom generations
sought throughout the ages long;
promised by the ancient prophets,
justice for a world of wrong,
God's salvation for the faithful:
him we praise in endless song
evermore and evermore.

3 Happy is that day for ever
when, by God the Spirit's grace,
lowly Mary, virgin mother,
bore the saviour of our race.
Man and child, the world's redeemer
now displays his sacred face,
evermore and evermore.

4 Praise him, heaven of heavens,
praise him, angels in the height;
priests and prophets, bow before him,
saints who longed to see this sight.
Let no human voice be silent,
in his glory hearts unite
evermore and evermore.

5 Christ be praised with God the Father,
and the Holy Spirit, praised!
hymns of worship, high thanksgiving
echo through a world amazed:
Honour, majesty, dominion!
songs of victory be raised
evermore and evermore.

106
From Psalm 46
© Richard Bewes / Jubilate Hymns

1 God is our strength and refuge,
our present help in trouble;
and we therefore will not fear,
though the earth should change!
Though mountains shake and tremble,
though swirling floods are raging,
God the Lord of hosts is with us evermore!

2 There is a flowing river,
within God's holy city;
God is in the midst of her –
she shall not be moved!
God's help is swiftly given,
thrones vanish at his presence –
God the Lord of hosts is with us evermore!

3 Come, see the works of our maker,
learn of his deeds all-powerful:
wars will cease across the world
when he shatters the spear!
Be still and know your creator,
uplift him in the nations –
God the Lord of hosts is with us evermore!

107
From In dulci jubilo (fourteenth century)
J M Neale (1818–1866)

1 Good Christians all, rejoice
with heart and soul and voice!
listen now to what we say,
Jesus Christ is born today;
ox and ass before him bow
and he is in the manger now:
Christ is born today;
Christ is born today!

2 Good Christians all, rejoice
with heart and soul and voice!
hear the news of endless bliss,
Jesus Christ was born for this:
he has opened heaven's door
and we are blessed for evermore!
Christ was born for this;
Christ was born for this.

3 Good Christians all, rejoice
with heart and soul and voice!
now you need not fear the grave;
Jesus Christ was born to save:
come at his most gracious call
to find salvation, one and all:
Christ was born to save;
Christ was born to save!

108
Traditional (eighteenth century)
© in this version Jubilate Hymns

1 God rest you merry, gentlemen,
let nothing you dismay!
for Jesus Christ our saviour
was born on Christmas Day,
to save us all from Satan's power
when we were gone astray:
O tidings of comfort and joy,
comfort and joy!
O tidings of comfort and joy!

2 At Bethlehem in Judah
the holy babe was born;
they laid him in a manger
on this most happy morn:
at which his mother Mary
did neither fear nor scorn:
  O tidings of comfort and joy,
  comfort and joy!
  O tidings of comfort and joy!

3 From God our heavenly Father
a holy angel came;
the shepherds saw the glory
and heard the voice proclaim
that Christ was born in Bethlehem –
and Jesus is his name:
  O tidings of comfort and joy . . .

4 Fear not, then said the angel,
let nothing cause you fright;
to you is born a saviour
in David's town tonight,
to free all those who trust in him
from Satan's power and might:
  O tidings of comfort and joy . . .

5 The shepherds at these tidings
rejoiced in heart and mind,
and on the darkened hillside
they left their flocks behind,
and went to Bethlehem straightway
this holy child to find:
  O tidings of comfort and joy . . .

6 And when to Bethlehem they came
where Christ the infant lay:
they found him in a manger
where oxen fed on hay,
and there beside her newborn child
his mother knelt to pray:
  O tidings of comfort and joy . . .

7 Now to the Lord sing praises,
all people in this place!
With Christian love and fellowship
each other now embrace,
and let this Christmas festival
all bitterness displace:
  O tidings of comfort and joy . . .

109
J M Neale (1818–1866)
© in this version Word & Music / Jubilate Hymns

1 ALL
Good king Wenceslas looked out
  on the Feast of Stephen,
when the snow lay round about,
  deep, and crisp, and even:
brightly shone the moon that night,
  though the frost was cruel,
when a poor man came in sight,
  gathering winter fuel.

2 KING
'Hither, page, and stand by me!
  If you know it, telling:
yonder poor man – who is he,
  where and what his dwelling?'
PAGE
'Sir, he lives a good way hence,
  underneath the mountain;
right against the forest fence
  by Saint Agnes' fountain.'

3 KING
'Bring me food, and bring me wine,
  bring me pine logs hither:
you and I will see him dine,
  when we take them thither.'
ALL
Page and monarch forth they went,
  forth they went together,
through the wild wind's loud lament
  and the bitter weather.

4 PAGE
'Sir, the night is darker now,
  and the wind grows stronger;
fails my heart – I know not how,
  I can go no longer.'
KING
'Mark my footsteps well, my page,
  follow in them boldly:
you shall find the winter's rage
  chills your blood less coldly.'

5 ALL
In his master's steps he trod
  where the snow lay even,
strong to do the will of God
  in the hope of heaven:
therefore, Christians all, be sure,
  grace and wealth possessing,
you that now will bless the poor
  shall yourselves find blessing.

110
© Mollie Knight and
Word & Music / Jubilate Hymns

1 Greetings, Christian friends and neighbours!
We with Bethlehem's shepherds say
'Welcome to the baby Jesus,
born this happy Christmas Day!'

2 Thank the Father for his mercy,
for the gift of peace on earth,
for the glorious hope of heaven
brought to us through Jesus' birth.

3 Bring your gifts – with joy present them
to the child, the holy One;
give your lives in love and service
to God's true and only Son.

4 Happy those who mark this season
mindful of the world's great need;
happy all who love our saviour,
serving him in word and deed.

5 So then, Christian friends and neighbours,
   celebrate! as well you may;
   sing to greet our saviour Jesus,
   born this happy Christmas Day.

111
Traditional
© in this version Word & Music / Jubilate Hymns

1 Good Christian people, rise and sing
   to greet the news the angels bring;
   good Christian people, rise and sing
   to greet the news the angels bring:
     news of great joy for all the earth,
     news of our holy saviour's birth!

2 Rejoice and be no longer sad,
   for Christ is born to make us glad;
   rejoice and be no longer sad,
   for Christ is born to make us glad:
     his power will drive away our sin,
     his lowly birth our love shall win.

3 Now in our darkness shines the light
   which made the angels sing that night;
   now in our darkness shines the light
   which made the angels sing that night.
     Glory to God! good-will and peace
     be to us all, and never cease!

112
© Mollie Knight / Jubilate Hymns

1 Happy day of great rejoicing!
   We proclaim a saviour's birth,
   for a child lies in a manger –
   Jesus Christ is born on earth.
   Gladly come, in worship kneeling
   by the cradle of the Son;
     sing with joy, ring out your praises,
     'Welcome to the holy One!'

2 Prince of peace, God's Word incarnate,
   with the poor identified;
   all his riches and his glory
   for love's sake are laid aside.
   Jesus comes to his creation,
   loving saviour, God's dear Son:
     sing with joy . . .

3 Hear the message of salvation
   Jesus brings to every race,
   see the infant who embodies
   God's great glory and his grace.
   Purest light will reach dark places
   through the love of Christ the Son:
     sing with joy . . .

113
J Montgomery (1771–1854)

1 Hail to the Lord's anointed,
   great David's greater son!
   Hail, in the time appointed
   his reign on earth begun!
   He comes to break oppression,
   to set the captive free,
   to take away transgression
   and rule in equity.

2 He comes with comfort speedy
   to those who suffer wrong;
   to save the poor and needy
   and help the weak be strong:
   to give them songs for sighing,
   their darkness turn to light,
   whose souls, condemned and dying,
   are precious in his sight.

3 He shall come down like showers
   upon the fruitful earth;
   and love, joy, hope, like flowers
   spring in his path to birth:
   before him on the mountains
   shall peace, the herald, go;
   and righteousness in fountains
   from hill to valley flow.

4 Kings shall bow down before him
   and gold and incense bring;
   all nations shall adore him,
   his praise all people sing:
   to him shall prayer unceasing
   and daily vows ascend;
   his kingdom still increasing,
   a kingdom without end.

5 In all the world victorious,
   he on his throne shall rest;
   from age to age more glorious,
   all-blessing and all-blessed:
   the tide of time shall never
   his covenant remove;
   his name shall stand for ever,
   his changeless name of love.

114
© Michael Perry / Jubilate Hymns

1 Happy Christmas, everybody!
   all the world is singing;
   come to worship, everybody,
   praise and glory bringing:
     Come to greet the Lord with joy;
     come to worship and adore him . . .

2 Happy Christmas, everybody!
   join the people praying;
   God is speaking, everybody –
   hear what love is saying:
     Come to greet . . .

3 Happy Christmas, everybody!
   God's new day is dawning;
   meet the saviour, everybody –
   Christ is born this morning:
     Come to greet . . .

   Happy Christmas, everybody!
   Christ is born this morning.

115
C Wesley (1707–1788) and others

1 Hark! the herald angels sing
glory to the new-born King;
peace on earth and mercy mild,
God and sinners reconciled!
Joyful all you nations rise,
join the triumph of the skies;
with the angelic host proclaim,
'Christ is born in Bethlehem':
  Hark! the herald angels sing
  glory to the new-born King.

2 Christ, by highest heaven adored,
Christ, the everlasting Lord!
late in time behold him come,
offspring of a virgin's womb;
veiled in flesh the Godhead see,
hail the incarnate Deity!
pleased as man with us to dwell,
Jesus our Emmanuel:
  Hark! the herald . . .

3 Hail the heaven-born Prince of peace,
hail the Sun of righteousness;
light and life to all he brings,
risen with healing in his wings:
mild, he lays his glory by,
born that we no more may die;
born to raise us from the earth,
born to give us second birth:
  Hark! the herald . . .

116
Mosie Lister
© Lillenas Publications / Thankyou Music †

1 Have you seen the little Child
  born in Bethlehem this night?
Have you seen the little Child,
  Mary's new-born Son?

2 Did you hear the angels sing,
  'Glory to the new-born King'?
Did you hear the praises ring
  for Mary's new-born Son?

3 Did you kneel in Bethlehem?
  Did you bow and worship him –
born the Saviour of us all,
  Mary's new-born Son?

4 Have you seen the little Child
  born in Bethlehem this night?
Have you seen the little Child,
  Mary's new-born Son?

117
Jimmy Owens
© Lexicon Music Incorporated / Word Music (UK) †

1 He is born, our Lord and saviour:
he is born, our heavenly king:
give him honour, give him glory,
earth rejoice and heaven sing!
Born to be our sanctuary,
born to bring us light and peace;
for our sins to bring forgiveness,
from our guilt to bring release.

2 He who is from everlasting
now becomes the incarnate Word;
he whose name endures for ever
now is born the Son of God:
born to bear our griefs and sorrows,
born to banish hate and strife;
born to bear the sin of many,
born to give eternal life!

3 Hail, the holy One of Israel,
chosen heir to David's throne;
hail the brightness of his rising –
to his light the gentiles come:
plunderer of Satan's kingdom,
downfall of his evil power;
rescuer of all his people,
conqueror in death's dark hour!

4 He shall rule with righteous judgement,
and his godly rule extend;
governor among the nations,
his great kingdom has no end:
he shall reign, the king of glory,
higher than the kings of earth –
alleluia, alleluia!
praise we now his holy birth!

118
Unknown

1 He who made the starry skies
sleeping in a stable lies,
ruler of the centuries:
  humbly clad king of kings,
  joy of heaven to earth brings,
  dear above all earthly things.

2 Joseph brings a garment there,
Mary wraps her child so fair,
rests him while she sings a prayer:
  humbly clad . . .

3 While we run this earthly race,
then throughout all time and space,
may he grant us hope and grace.

119
Joan Parsons
© Thankyou Music †

1 He holds the key to salvation –
Jesus is over all;
he is the Lord of creation:
  Alleluia, alleluia,
  alleluia, alleluia, Lord!

3 He is the rock ever standing –
no-one could break him down;
he is the truth everlasting:
  Alleluia . . .

He is a light in the darkness,
and all shall see his face;
he breaks our chains to redeem us:
  Alleluia . . .

All power to him who is mighty,
all praise to him who is God;
all glory now and forever:
  Alleluia . . .

120

Georgian Banov and Mark Pendergrass
© Sparrow Song / Cherry Lane Music †

1 Hear the chimes (hear the chimes)
as they ring (as they ring),
they foretell (they foretell)
of the King (of the King);
he is born (he is born),
let us bring (let us bring)
every gift (every gift)
as we sing (as we sing)
to the King.
　　Hosanna! bring praises to the King.
　　Alleluia! let your praises ring.

2 Every land (every land),
every town (every town),
every home (every home),
every heart (every heart):
ring it out (ring it out),
sing and shout (sing and shout)
dance and sing (dance and sing),
let it ring (let it ring)
to the King.
　　Hosanna . . .

122

After the Jugoslavian carol
© Michael Perry / Jubilate Hymns

1 Hear the skies around
fill with joyful sound,
and the praise of angels ring;
hear the skies . . .
　　Singing 'Glory in the highest,'
　　singing 'Glory to the King!'
Hear the skies . . .

2 'To the earth be peace,
fear and sorrow cease!'
is the birthday news they bring.
'To the earth . . .
　　Singing 'Glory in the highest,'
　　singing 'Glory to the King!'
'To the earth . . .

3 Banish all dismay,
for on Christmas Day
there's a song of praise to sing;
Banish all dismay . . .
　　Singing 'Glory in the highest,'
　　singing 'Glory to the King!'
Banish all dismay . . .

121

© Timothy Dudley-Smith †

1 Hear how the bells of Christmas play!
Well may they ring for joy and say,
　　O praise him, alleluia;
God has fulfilled his promised word,
born is our Saviour and our Lord,
　　O praise him, O praise him,
　　alleluia, alleluia, alleluia!

2 Let all the waiting earth rejoice,
lift every heart and every voice,
　　O praise him, alleluia;
sing now the song to angels given,
glory to God in highest heaven!
　　O praise him . . .

3 As through the silence of the skies
shepherds in wonder heard arise,
　　O praise him, alleluia;
So may we hear again with them
songs in the night at Bethlehem,
　　O praise him . . .

4 All nature sang at Jesus' birth,
Hail the Creator come to earth!
　　O praise him, alleluia;
sun, moon and shining stars above,
tell out the story of his love,
　　O praise him . . .

5 Hear how the bells of Christmas play!
Well may they ring for joy and say,
　　O praise him, alleluia;
come now to worship and adore,
Christ is our peace for evermore,
　　O praise him . . .

123/124

© Timothy Dudley-Smith †

1 Holy child, how still you lie!
safe the manger, soft the hay;
faint upon the eastern sky
breaks the dawn of Christmas Day.

2 Holy child, whose birthday brings
shepherds from their field and fold,
angel choirs and eastern kings,
myrrh and frankincense and gold:

3 Holy child, what gift of grace
from the Father freely willed!
In your infant form we trace
all God's promises fulfilled.

4 Holy child, whose human years
span like ours delight and pain;
one in human joys and tears,
one in all but sin and stain:

5 Holy child, so far from home,
all the lost to seek and save:
to what dreadful death you come,
to what dark and silent grave!

6 Holy child, before whose name
powers of darkness faint and fall;
conquered, death and sin and shame –
Jesus Christ is Lord of all!

7 Holy child, how still you lie!
safe the manger, soft the hay;
clear upon the eastern sky
breaks the dawn of Christmas Day.

125
From Isaiah 52
Leonard E Smith Jnr
© Thankyou Music †

1 How lovely on the mountains are the feet of him
who brings good news, good news,
proclaiming peace,
    announcing news of happiness:
our God reigns, our God reigns!
    Our God reigns, our God reigns,
    our God reigns, our God reigns!

2 You watchmen lift your voices joyfully as one,
shout for your king, your king;
see eye to eye the Lord restoring Zion:
your God reigns, your God reigns!
    Your God . . .

3 Waste places of Jerusalem
    break forth with joy –
we are redeemed, redeemed;
the Lord has saved and comforted his people:
your God reigns, your God reigns!
    Your God . . .

4 Ends of the earth,
    see the salvation of your God –
Jesus is Lord, is Lord!
Before the nations he has bared his holy arm:
your God reigns, your God reigns!
    Your God . . .

126 © Philip Warren / Jubilate Hymns
    Holy, holy Lord,
    holy, holy Lord,
    God of power and love.

1 Heaven and earth are full of your glory,
hosanna in the highest.
    Holy, holy Lord . . .

2 Born for us in Bethlehem,
the Saviour of the world.
    Holy, holy Lord . . .

3 Sleeping there among the hay,
the Prince of peace has come.
    Holy, holy Lord . . .

4 Heaven and earth are full of your glory,
hosanna in the highest,
    Holy, holy Lord,
    holy, holy Lord!

127 © Timothy Dudley-Smith †

1 Hush you, my baby,
the night wind is cold,
the lambs from the hillside
are safe in the fold:
sleep with the starlight
and wake with the morn –
    the Lord of all glory
    a baby is born.

2 Hush you, my baby,
so soon to be grown,
watching by moonlight
on mountains alone,
toiling and travelling –
so sleep while you can,
    till the Lord of all glory
    is seen as a man.

3 Hush you, my baby,
the years will not stay,
the cross on the hilltop
the end of the way;
dim through the darkness,
in grief and in gloom,
    the Lord of all glory
    lies cold in the tomb.

4 Hush you, my baby,
the Father on high
in power and dominion
the darkness puts by;
bright from the shadows,
the seal and the stone,
    the Lord of all glory
    returns to his own.

5 Hush you, my baby,
the sky turns to gold,
the lambs on the hillside
are loose from the fold;
fast fades the midnight
and new springs the morn,
    the Lord of all glory
    a Saviour is born.

128
R Croo (1534)
© in this version Word & Music / Jubilate hymns
    Hush, do not cry,
    my little tiny child:
    Lullaby, lullaby!

1 O brothers, tell
what ill befell
Bethlehem's town this day;
let grief recite
these infants' plight,
sorrow and sore dismay.
    * Hush, do not cry, . . .

2 O sisters too,
what may we do
and save from death today
this poor young thing
to whom we sing:
'Lullaby, lullalay'?
    * Hush, do not cry, . . .

3 Herod the king,
in his raging,
gave his command this day:
his men of might
in his own sight
all little boys to slay.
    * Hush, do not cry, . . .

4 Then woe is me,
poor child, to see
this sad and sorry day;
from your parting
we say nor sing,
'Lullaby, lullalay.'
 * Hush, do not cry, . . .

* The repeated refrain may be omitted

129
© Michael Perry / Jubilate Hymns

Hush, little baby; peace, little boy
slumbering in the hay;
dream while we carol tidings of joy,
Jesus of Christmas Day.

1 Angels will tell news of good cheer,
glory will light the sky;
shepherds will kneel wondering here,
worshipping God most high.
Hush, little baby . . .

2 Joseph will guard, Mary will smile,
holding in sweet embrace
heaven's true Lord, here for a while,
Jesus, God's gift of grace.
Hush, little baby . . .

3 Wise men from far, soon they will come,
worship and gifts they bring:
incense for prayer, myrrh for a tomb,
gold to reveal a king.
Hush, little baby . . .

130
Martin Nystrom
© Integrity's Hosanna! Music †

I will come and bow down at your feet,
Lord Jesus;
in you presence is fulness of joy.
There is nothing,
there is no-one to compare with you:
I take pleasure in worshipping you, Lord.

131
Appalachian carol
© in this version Word & Music / Jubilate Hymns

1 I wonder as I wander, out under the sky,
why Jesus the saviour came down from on high
for us lowly people to suffer and die –
I wonder as I wander, out under the sky.

2 When Jesus was born – it was in a cow's stall –
came angels and shepherds
and wise men and all,
and from the high heaven a star's light did fall,
the wonderful promise of God to recall.

3 If Jesus had wanted for any one thing –
a star in the sky, or a bird on the wing,
or all of God's angels in heaven to sing –
he surely could have it, for he was the king.

4 I wonder as I wander, out under the sky,
why Jesus the saviour came down from on high
for us lowly people to suffer and die –
I wonder as I wander, out under the sky.

132
© Elizabeth Bennett

1 If I'd been there in Bethlehem,
if I had seen that star,
would I write a book about it;
would I go that far?
And if I'd been a traveller,
and you said 'Follow me!'
would I go to where you led,
and take you seriously?
Star bright, gleaming white,
thoughts I have of you tonight;
star bright, gleaming white,
shine on us all this Christmas night!

2 If I'd been an astrologer,
a prophet or a king,
would I find myself disturbed
by such a gentle thing?
If you, dear Jesus, had a chance
to turn and run away,
would you stay to live that life,
and still be here today?
Star bright . . .

133
From John 1
Russell Hodgson
© Mustard Seed Music †

1 In the beginning, the Word already was;
the Word dwelt with God,
the Word and God were one;
in him was life,
the life was the light of men;
and the light shines in the darkness.
The light of Christ has come into the world,
the light of Christ is here;
the light of Christ has come into the world,
the light of Christ is here!

2 So the Word became flesh
and came to dwell among us;
we have seen his glory,
such glory as befits the Father's Son.
No one has ever seen God,
but the Son has made him known:
and the light shines in the darkness.
The light of Christ . . .

3 He is our messiah, he is God the Son;
he will lead his children
on and on and on and on.
The light of Christ . . .

134
© Michael Perry / Jubilate Hymns

1 In a stable, in a manger,
lies a baby – our true saviour:
hear the carol that we sing you,
and the tidings that we bring you.
There's a light in the heavens this morning
and a song for the angels to sing;
in a stable, in a manger,
lies a baby – our true saviour.

2 There the virgin mother Mary
tends her infant – oh so gently;
and the beauty of the Godhead
shines around him – her belovèd.
There's a light in the heavens this morning
and a song for the angels to sing;
in a stable, in a manger,
lies a baby – our true saviour.

3 Let the mighty faint and tremble
at the triumph of the humble;
and the guilty leave their sighing
where the sinner's hope is lying.
There's a light . . .

2 In the manger lay this babe of love
through the night;
shepherds came in joy and haste
to see God's own light.
How the shepherds sang 'Allelu'!
Sing to Jesus, sing 'Allelu'!

3 Wise men, ox and ass,
come, join the praise of his birth;
children of the light proclaim the good news
to the earth.
Lift your voices, sing 'Allelu',
sing to Jesus, sing 'Allelu'!

'Allelu, allelu, allelu'!

135 C G Rossetti (1830–1894)

1 In the bleak mid-winter
frosty wind made moan,
earth stood hard as iron,
water like a stone;
snow had fallen, snow on snow,
snow on snow,
in the bleak mid-winter
long ago.

2 Heaven cannot hold him,
nor earth sustain;
heaven and earth shall flee away
when he comes to reign:
in the bleak mid-winter
a stable-place sufficed
God, the Lord almighty,
Jesus Christ.

3 Enough for him whom cherubim
worship night and day –
a breastful of milk,
and a manger full of hay;
enough for him whom angels
fall down before –
the wise men and the shepherds
who adore!

4 What can I give him,
poor as I am?
If I were a shepherd
I would give a lamb,
if I were a wise man
I would do my part;
yet what I can I give him –
give my heart.

136 Wiley Beveridge and Glenna McLane
© Celebration Services / Thankyou Music †

1 In the little town of Bethlehem long ago
a little babe was born to save the world
from all woe.
How the angels sang 'Allelu'!
Sing to Jesus, sing 'Allelu'!

137 From Isaiah 9
© Michael Perry / Jubilate Hymns

1 In the darkness of the night
the people walk in sorrow;
they have not seen, nor can they know
the light that dawns tomorrow.
For a Child is born to us,
to us a Son is given:
his holy name – the Prince of peace,
the Mighty God of heaven.

2 In the darkness of the night
a host of angels gather
to greet the Wonderful, the Wise,
the Everlasting Father.
For a Child . . .

3 In the darkness of the night
where Judah's hills lie dreaming,
the virgin mother of the Christ
beholds our world's redeeming.
For a Child . . .

138 From the Polish
E M G Reed (1885–1933)

1 Infant holy, infant lowly,
for his bed a cattle stall;
oxen lowing, little knowing
Christ the babe is Lord of all.
Swift are winging angels singing,
nowells ringing, tidings bringing:
Christ the babe is Lord of all;
Christ the babe is Lord of all!

2 Flocks were sleeping, shepherds keeping
vigil till the morning new,
saw the glory, heard the story –
tidings of a gospel true.
Thus rejoicing, free from sorrow,
praises voicing greet tomorrow:
Christ the babe was born for you;
Christ the babe was born for you!

139
© David Mowbray / Jubilate Hymns

1 Into darkness light has broken,
  Christ has been born!
out of silence God has spoken;
  Christ has been born!
Prince of peace, the nations greet him,
thrones and powers cannot defeat him:
sing for joy and come to meet him.
  Christ has been born!

2 For to us a son is given,
  Christ has been born!
treasured gift to earth from heaven;
  Christ has been born!
wondrous counsellor to guide us,
judge when justice is denied us,
everlasting God beside us.
  Christ has been born!

3 Promised child – we tell the story –
  Christ has been born!
Son of David, Israel's glory:
  Christ has been born!
in this child our God has sought us,
wisdom from on high has taught us,
hope and healing now has brought us.
  Christ has been born!

140/141
E H Sears (1810–1876)
© in this version Word & Music /
Jubilate Hymns

1 It came upon the midnight clear,
that glorious song of old,
from angels bending near the earth
to touch their harps of gold:
'Through all the earth, goodwill and peace
from heaven's all-gracious king!'
The world in solemn stillness lay
to hear the angels sing.

2 With sorrow brought by sin and strife
the world has suffered long
and, since the angels sang, have passed
two thousand years of wrong;
the nations, still at war, hear not
the love-song which they bring:
O hush the noise, and cease the strife
to hear the angels sing!

3 And those whose journey now is hard,
whose hope is burning low,
who tread the rocky path of life
with painful steps and slow:
O listen to the news of love
which makes the heavens ring!
O rest beside the weary road
and hear the angels sing!

4 And still the days are hastening on –
by prophets seen of old –
towards the fulness of the time
when comes the age foretold:
then earth and heaven renewed shall see
the prince of peace, their king;
and all the world repeat the song
which now the angels sing.

142
After an Appalachian carol
© in this version Word & Music / Jubilate Hymns

1 It was in Judah's land
by God's almighty hand
that Jesus Christ was born in a stable:
  in a stable,
  in a stable,
  that Jesus Christ was born in a stable.

2 For by his mother's hand
he was wrapped in swathing band
and in a manger laid in a stable:
  in a stable,
  in a stable,
  and in a manger laid in a stable.

143
© Michael Perry / Jubilate Hymns

1 Jesus, child of Mary born,
Son of God and Lord most high;
come to wear a crown of thorn,
bravely come to die.

2 To this place of pain and fear
love descends in human guise;
God in Christ self-emptied here,
foolishness most wise:

3 Infant in a manger laid,
wrapped about with peasant shawl;
gift of grace so freely made,
saviour for us all.

4 Angel hosts the skies adorn,
we with shepherds glorify
Jesus, child of Mary born,
Son of God most high.

144
After J Cennick (1718–1755)
C Wesley (1707–1788) and M Madan (1726–1790)
© in this version Jubilate Hymns

1 Jesus comes with clouds descending –
see the Lamb for sinners slain!
thousand thousand saints attending
join to sing the glad refrain:
  Alleluia, alleluia, alleluia!
God appears on earth to reign.

2 Every eye shall then behold him
robed in awesome majesty;
those who jeered at him and sold him,
pierced and nailed him to the tree,
  shamed and grieving . . .
shall their true Messiah see.

3 All the wounds of cross and passion
still his glorious body bears;
cause of endless exultation
to his ransomed worshippers.
  With what gladness . . .
we shall see the Saviour's scars!

4 Yes, Amen! let all adore you
high on your eternal throne;
crowns and empires fall before you –
claim the kingdom for your own.
  Come, Lord Jesus . . .
everlasting God, come down!

145

From Job 19 and Ephesians 1
Peter and Diane Fung
© Thankyou Music †

Jesus Christ our great redeemer,
mighty victor and strong deliverer,
king of kings and Lord of lords,
we praise you, praise your name –
  Alleluia, alleluia;
King of kings and Lord of lords –
  Alleluia, alleluia!
your victory is assured.

146

After German authors
© Michael Perry / Jubilate Hymns

1 Jesus Christ the Lord is born,
  all the bells are ringing!
  angels greet the holy One
    and shepherds hear them singing,
    and shepherds hear them singing.

2 'Go to Bethlehem today,
  find your king and saviour:
  glory be to God on high,
    to earth his peace and favour,
    to earth his peace and favour!'

3 Held within a cattle stall,
  loved by love maternal,
  see the master of us all,
    our Lord of lords eternal,
    our Lord of lords eternal.

4 Soon shall come the wise men three,
  rousing Herod's anger;
  mother's hearts shall broken be
    and Mary's son in danger,
    and Mary's son in danger.

5 Death from life and life from death,
  our salvation's story:
  let all living things give breath
    to Christmas songs of glory,
    to Christmas songs of glory!

147

From Luke 2 (The Song of Simeon / Nunc dimittis)
© Michael Perry / Jubilate Hymns

1 Jesus, hope of every nation,
  light of heaven upon our way;
  promise of the world's salvation,
  spring of life's eternal day!

2 Saints by faith on God depending
  wait to see Messiah born;
  sin's oppressive night is ending
  in the glory of the dawn!

3 Look, he comes! – the long-awaited
  Christ, redeemer, living Word;
  hope and faith are vindicated
  as with joy we greet the Lord.

4 Glory in the highest heaven
  to the Father, Spirit, Son;
  and on earth let praise be given
  to our God, the Three-in-one!

148

Paul Inwood
© Magnificat Music †

ADVENT

1 Jesus, Lamb of God and source of life;
  Jesus, loving bearer of our sins:
    hear our prayer, have mercy,
    hear our prayer, have mercy,
    give us your peace.

2 Jesus, coming near to bring us joy;
  Jesus, Son of God, Emmanuel:
    hear our prayer . . .

3 Jesus, bringing hope to all who fear;
  Jesus, bringing strength to all who mourn:
    hear our prayer . . .

4 Jesus, Saviour heralded by John:
  Jesus, son of David's house and line:
    hear our prayer . . .

CHRISTMAS

1 Jesus, Lamb of God, the Word made flesh;
  Jesus, Son of God come down on earth:
    hear our prayer, have mercy,
    hear our prayer, have mercy,
    give us your peace.

2 Jesus, King of glory, Prince of peace,
  Jesus, shining in our darkened world:
    hear our prayer . . .

3 Jesus, King of angels, Lord of joy;
  Jesus, born to save the world from sin:
    hear our prayer . . .

149

Naida Hearn
© Scripture in Song / Thankyou Music †

Jesus, name above all names,
beautiful saviour, glorious Lord;
Emmanuel – God is with us!
blessèd redeemer, living Word.

150

© Michael Perry / Jubilate Hymns

1 Jesus, saviour, holy child,
    sleep tonight,
  slumber deep till morning light.
    Lullaby, our joy, our treasure,
    all our hope and all our pleasure:
  at the cradle where you lie
  we will worship – lullaby!

2 From your Father's home you come
    to this earth,
  by your lowly manger birth!
    Child of God, our nature sharing;
    Son of Man, our sorrows bearing:
  rich, yet here among the poor:
  Christ the Lord, whom we adore!

3 Now to heaven's glory song
    we reply
  with a Christmas lullaby.
    Hush, the eternal Lord is sleeping
    close in Mary's tender keeping:
  babe on whom the angels smiled –
  Jesus, saviour, holy child.

151

1 Jesus was born in a stable,
there was no room in the inn;
he had a stall for a cradle,
   that was good enough for him.

2 Cattle asleep in the corner,
Joseph kept watch from within.
Can you imagine the sorrow?
   That was good enough for him.

3 No kingly robes for his vesture,
no royal hall for this one;
but Mary cradled her treasure,
   for he was God's dear Son.

4 Jesus was born in a stable,
there was no room in the inn;
he has a stall for a cradle,
   that was good enough for him.

   And that was good enough for him.

152

1 Journey to Bethlehem, worship your king,
   worship your king, worship your king;
come with your praises and joyfully sing,
   joyfully sing, joyfully sing!

2 Come with your presents of honour and love,
   honour and love, honour and love;
this is the birthday of hope from above,
   hope from above, hope from above.

3 Come with your sorrow
         for wrongs you have done,
   wrongs you have done,
         wrongs you have done;
find your forgiveness in God's only Son,
   God's only Son, God's only Son.

4 Come with your praises and joyfully sing,
   joyfully sing, joyfully sing;
journey to Bethlehem, worship your king,
   worship your king, worship your king!

153

1 Joy to the world – the Lord has come:
let earth receive her king,
let every heart prepare him room
   and heaven and nature sing,
   and heaven and nature sing,
   and heaven, and heaven and nature sing!

2 Joy to the earth – the saviour reigns:
your sweetest songs employ
while fields and streams and hills and plains
   repeat the sounding joy,
   repeat the sounding joy,
   repeat, repeat the sounding joy.

3 He rules the world with truth and grace,
and makes the nations prove
the glories of his righteousness,
   the wonders of his love,
   the wonders of his love,
   the wonders, wonders of his love.

154

King of kings and Lord of lords,
   Glory, alleluia!
King of kings . . .
Jesus, Prince of peace,
   Glory, alleluia!
Jesus, Prince . . .

155

1 Kings came riding from the East,
searching for the Prince of peace;
then king Herod, wicked man,
schemed and plotted evil plan.

2 Herod told them: 'Find the babe;
come and tell me where he's laid:
I will go there, kneel me down,
offer him my golden crown.'

3 But all he wanted was his blood,
to have this infant gone for good.
Quickly riding through the sand,
kings left Herod's desert land.

156/157

1 Let the desert sing and the wasteland flower,
for the glory of the God in its light and power
shall be seen on the hills
      where he comes to save!

2 Then the blind shall see and the deaf shall hear
and the lame shall leap like the fallow deer
and the voice of the dumb shall shout aloud.

3 When the ransomed walk
         with their Lord that day
on the perfect road called the Sacred Way,
every tear shall give place to a song of joy!
   a song of joy!

158

1 Let all the earth hear his voice,
let the people rejoice
at the sound of his name;
let all the valleys and hills burst with joy,
and the trees of the field
clap their hands.
   Justice and love he will bring to the world,
   his kingdom will never fail;
   held like a two-edged sword in our hand,
   his word and truth shall prevail, shall prevail!

2 Let all the earth hear his voice,
    let the prisoners rejoice –
    he is coming to save.
    Satan's dark strongholds crash down
    as with prayer we surround,
    as the cross we proclaim.
        Justice and love he will bring to the world,
        his kingdom will never fail;
        held like a two-edged sword in our hand,
        his word and truth shall prevail, shall prevail!

3 Let all the earth hear his song;
    sing it loud, sing it strong –
    it's the song of his praise.
    Silent no more, we cry out –
    let the world hear the shout:
    in the earth the Lord reigns.
        Justice and love . . .

159 From Psalm 68
Graham Kendrick
© Thankyou Music †

Let God arise,
and let his enemies be scattered,
and let those who hate him
flee before him;
let God arise,
and let his enemies be scattered,
and let those who hate him
flee away.

MEN
But let the righteous be glad;
let them exult before God,
let them rejoice with gladness,
building up a highway for the king.
We go in the name of the Lord:
let the shout go up in the name of the Lord!

WOMEN
The righteous be glad,
let them exult before God;
O let them rejoice
for the king
in the name of the Lord!

160 Mike and Claire McIntosh
© Northwest Church / Thankyou Music †

1 Let praises ring, let praises ring,
    lift voices up to love him;
    lift hearts and hands to touch him!
    O let praises ring,
    and fill the sky with anthems high
    that tell his excellency,
    as priests and kings who rule with him
    through all eternity!
        Let praises ring, let praises ring,
        to our glorious King!

2 Let praises ring, let praises ring,
    bow down in adoration;
    cry out his exaltation –
    O let praises ring,
    and lift the name above all names,
    till every nation knows
    the love of God has come to us –
    his mercy overflows!
        Let praises ring . . .

161 Steven Fry
© Birdwing Music / Cherry Lane Music Ltd †

Lift up your heads to the coming King;
bow before him and adore him,
        sing to his majesty:
let your praises be pure and holy,
giving glory to the King of kings.

162 From Psalm 24
Peter Fung
© Thankyou Music †

Lift up your heads, O you gates,
and be lifted up, you everlasting doors,
that the King of glory may come in.
    Who is the King of glory?
    Who is the King of glory?
    Who is the King of glory?
    The Lord of hosts mighty in battle!

    Who is the King . . .
    He is the King of Glory.

    Who is the King . . .
    He is the King of glory:
    the Lord of hosts,
    he is the King of glory!

163 After G Weissel (1590–1633)
and C Winkworth (1827–1878)
© in this version Word & Music / Jubilate Hymns

1 Lift up your heads, you mighty gates –
    behold, the Lord of glory waits,
    the King of kings is drawing near,
    the saviour of the world is here!

2 O blessed the land, the city blessed
    where Christ the ruler is confessed;
    O happy hearts and happy homes
    to whom this King in triumph comes!

3 Redeemer, come! – we open wide
    our hearts to you this Advent-tide:
    so let your Spirit guide us on
    until the glorious hope is won!

OR, AT CHRISTMAS
3 Redeemer, come! – we open wide
    our hearts to you this Christmastide:
    so let your Spirit guide us on
    until the glorious hope is won!

164 From Psalm 98 (*Cantate Domino*)
© Michael Perry / Jublate Hymns

1 Lift up your hearts to the Lord,
    break into songs of joy;
    let the sea roar, let the hills ring,
    shout his glorious name!

Harps and horns and trumpets, sound;
praise him, all the world around!
    O sing a new song;
    O sing a new song!

2 Bow down and worship the Lord,
   greet him who comes to reign;
   share his triumph, hear his judgement,
   see his marvellous works:
       Harps and horns . . .

3 Tell out the word of the Lord,
   speak of his saving power:
   sure his mercy, true his promise,
   great his wonderful love!
       Harps and horns . . .

165 © Michael Perry / Jubilate Hymns

1 Lift your heart and raise your voice;
   faithful people, come, rejoice:
   grace and power are shown on earth
   in the saviour's holy birth.
       Gloria!

2 Mortals, hear what angels say;
   shepherds, quickly make your way,
   finding truth in lowly guise,
   wisdom to confound the wise.
       Gloria!

3 Here he lies, the Lord of all;
   nature's king in cattle-stall,
   God of heaven to earth come down –
   cross for throne and thorn for crown.
       Gloria!

4 Lift your hearts and voices high:
   then shall glory fill the sky,
   Christ shall come and not be long,
   earth shall sing the angels' song –
       Gloria!

166 David J Hadden and Bob Sylvester © Restoration Music Ltd †

1 Living under the shadow of his wing
       we find security;
   standing in his presence we will bring
       our worship, worship, worship to the King.

2 Bowed in adoration at his feet
       we dwell in harmony,
   voices joined together that repeat:
       'Worthy, worthy, worthy is the Lamb!'

3 Heart to heart embracing in his love,
       we know his purity,
   raising worthy praise to him above:
       'Holy, holy, holy is the Lord!'

167 Anne Johnson © Eyes and Ears Music †

1 Light shining in the darkness,
   light that is the world's true light;
   light from the beginning,
   now as then, still shining bright.

People rejoice! the night is gone,
God's redeeming work begun
in the birth of his Son.

2 Love came to dwell among us,
   love made flesh at Bethlehem,
   love from the beginning,
   our divine Creator's theme.
       People rejoice . . .

3 Life full of truth and beauty,
   life as it was meant to be,
   life from the beginning,
   and into eternity.
       People rejoice . . .

168 Unknown

Light the candles round the world,
pray the light will never cease
till the nations of the world
take each other's hands in peace:
light the path and show the way,
every boy and every girl;
make the light as bright as day,
light the candles round the world!

1 Make each flame a loving heart,
   mother, father, daughter, son:
   all it takes is one to start
   for the world to be as one.
       Light the candles . . .

2 So I tell you this, my love:
   when you see the light appear
   it will drive away the dark,
   and there'll be nothing left to fear.
       Light the candles . . .

169 Garth Hewitt © Word Music (UK) †

1 Like a flicker in the darkness
   comes a mother's desperate cry;
   then a baby's voice in answer
   brings the coming of the light.
       Light a candle in the darkness,
       light a candle in the night;
       let the love of Jesus light us –
       light a candle in the night!

2 He did not come in wealth and grandeur,
   he did not stand with men of power,
   he had no status to commend him,
   he was homeless – he was poor.
       Like a candle . . .

3 But he came to heal the wounded,
   and he came to heal the scars
   of a world that's bruised and broken,
   where the image has been marred.
       Like a candle . . .

4 And we see him in the hungry
   and the homeless refugee,
   in the sick and dying children –
   his hands reach out for you and me.
       Like a candle . . .

5 And I feel his breath upon me,
and he whispers, 'Follow me!'
and he grants his fire within me,
says, 'Let it shine for all to see!'
    Light a candle in the darkness,
    light a candle in the night;
    let the love of Jesus light us –
    light a candle in the night!

170
Ted Sandquist
© Coronation Music Ltd †

1 Lion of Judah, on the throne,
I shout your name – let it be known
that you are the King of kings,
you are the Prince of peace:
may your kingdom's reign never cease.
    Hail to the king, hail to the king!

2 Lion of Judah, come to earth,
I want to thank you for your birth;
for the living Word,
for your death on the tree,
for your resurrection victory.
    Alleluia, alleluia!

3 Lion of Judah, come again,
take up your throne – Jerusalem;
bring release to this earth!
and the consummation of your kingdom's reign,
let it come!
    Maranatha, maranatha!

4 Lion of Judah, on the throne,
I shout your name – let it be known
that you are the King of kings,
you are the Prince of peace:
may your kingdom's reign never cease.
    Hail to the king, hail to the king!
    you are my king!

171
verse 1 L H Ward
© Boston Music Company Inc /
International Music Publications †
verse 2 © Jubilate Hymns

1 Little children, wake and listen!
songs are filling all the earth;
while the stars in heaven glisten,
hear the news of Jesus' birth.
Long ago, to lonely meadows
angels brought the message down;
still each year through midnight shadows
it is heard in every town.

2 Shepherds hurry to the stable
by the inn at Bethlehem,
run as fast as they are able
to the baby born for them.
People find the news amazing
as on that first Christmas morn:
let us join the shepherds praising
God, for Christ the king is born!

172
Eric Boswell
© Chappell & Company Limited /
International Music Publications †

1 Little donkey, little donkey,
on a dusty road,
got to keep on plodding onward
with your precious load:

2 Been a long time little donkey,
through the winter's night –
don't give up now, little donkey,
Bethlehem's in sight.
    Ring out those bells tonight,
    Bethlehem, Bethlehem;
    follow that star tonight,
    Bethlehem, Bethlehem!

3 Little donkey, little donkey,
had a heavy day –
little donkey, carry Mary
safely on her way.
    Ring out . . .

4 Little donkey, little donkey,
had a heavy day –
little donkey, carry Mary
safely on her way.

(* Little donkey, carry Mary
safely on her way;
little donkey, carry Mary
safely on her way.)

* Optional ending

173
Pamela Verrall
© B Feldman & Co. Ltd /
International Music Publications †

1 Long ago and far away
in Bethlehem, a mother lay
her new-born babe upon the hay.
He was the holy Jesus-child,
he was the holy Jesus.
    Nowell, nowell – let angels sing;
    nowell, nowell – let church bells ring;
    nowell, nowell – let everything sing
    alleluia to the baby boy!

2 Shepherds on the mountain cold
awoke when angel voices told,
'Go and leave your lambs in fold –
follow the star to Bethlehem;
follow the star to Bethlehem!'
    Nowell, nowell – let angels sing . . .

3 When they reached the open door
and saw that love had gone before,
they wondering knelt on dirty floor,
worshipping baby Jesus there,
worshipping baby Jesus.
    Nowell, nowell – let angels sing . . .

174

1 Long, long ago it happened;
the prophet Isaiah of old
to all the people of Judah
the birth of a king foretold:
Wonderful Counsellor, Mighty God,
Lord and Prince of peace –
Father everlasting
he should be all of these.
   'Glory to God in the highest!'
   thus the angels sang;
   and with Alleluias,
   loud the heavens rang.

2 Gabriel visited Mary –
a virgin most pure was she:
'You shall give birth to the Saviour
of mankind,' said he.
'How can this be,' she answered,
never a man knew I?'
'You have been chosen to bear
the Son of God most high.'
   to Christ our heavenly king.
   Glory to God . . .

3 Caesar Augustus had ordered
a census through all the land;
Mary and Joseph to Bethlehem
set out at this command:
straight to the inn they went then –
'No room at all,' they were told;
only the stable was offered them
to keep them from the cold.
   Glory to God . . .

4 So did our Lord Christ Jesus
come down to us on earth;
shepherds and travelling wise men
marvelled at his birth:
so, at this Christmas season,
cheerfully do we sing
honour and praise and glory
to Christ our heavenly king.
   'Glory to God in the highest,'
   sing at Christmas still,
   'and on earth be peace to all
   people of good-will!'

175

1 Long time ago in Bethlehem,
so the Holy Bible say,
Mary's boy-child, Jesus Christ,
was born on Christmas Day.
   Hark now, hear the angels sing –
   a new king born today!
   And we may live for evermore
   because of Christmas Day.
   Trumpets sound and angels sing –
   listen to what they say,
   that we may live for evermore
   because of Christmas Day.

2 While shepherds watch their flocks by night,
them see a bright new shining star;
them hear a choir sing –
the music seems to come from afar.

3 Now Joseph and his wife Mary
come to Bethlehem that night;
she have no place to bear her child –
not a single room was in sight.
   Hark now . . .

4 By and by they find a little nook
in a stable all forlorn,
and in a manger cold and dark,
Mary's little boy was born.

5 Long time ago in Bethlehem,
so the Holy Bible say,
Mary's boy-child, Jesus Christ,
was born on Christmas Day.
   Hark now . . .

   Yes, we may live for evermore
   because of Christmas Day.

176

1 Lord everlasting yet child born in Bethlehem,
Mary your mother and favoured indeed,
sharing our struggle, our grief and uncertainty,
shining as light of the world in its need:

2 Lord God among us –
   your strength found in gentleness,
greeted by shepherds in fields with their flock:
call us as servants, and send us as witnesses
to all our neighbours and places of work.

3 Lord of all lords and our promised deliverer,
worshipped by kings bringing gifts from afar:
guide with your wisdom all those in authority,
sparing the nations from hatred and war.

4 Lord, taking flight in a refugee family,
harrassed and threatened –
   the poor of the earth:
open our hearts to the outcast and prisoner,
bringing compassion and justice to birth.

5 Lord, lowly stooping
   to raise up your broken-ones –
love at the crib and the cross are the same:
help us with angels your great name to glorify,
and with archangels that love to proclaim!

177

1 Look away to Bethlehem,
seek the star up in the sky;
follow where it sends its silver beam,
listen for a lullaby:
find the stable bleak and bare,
gently open up the door,
gaze with wonder at the holy Babe –
he whom heaven and earth adore.

'Alleluia,' sing the angels,
'Peace on earth, goodwill to men!'
'Alleluia,' sing the angels:
'Look away to Bethlehem!'

2 Wandering shepherds saw the star,
on that night so long ago;
left their flocks to find the holy child
sent from heaven here below:
princes sought a palace fair,
bearing gifts of untold worth,
but they knelt beside a humble throne
when the Lord came to the earth.
    Alleluia . . .

3 Let the Christmas bells ring out
from each steeple in the sky;
let their music swell until it blends
with the angel choirs on high:
look away to Bethlehem,
seek the star up in the sky,
follow where it sends its silver beam,
listen for a lullaby!
    Alleluia . . .

    Look away to Bethlehem!

178 Graham Kendrick
         © Thankyou Music †

1 Look to the skies, there's a celebration;
lift up your heads, join the angel song,
for our Creator becomes our saviour,
as a baby born!
Angels amazed bow in adoration:
'Glory to God in the highest heaven!' –
send the good news out to every nation,
for our hope has come.
    Worship the king – come, see his brightness;
    worship the king, his wonders tell:
    Jesus our king is born today –
    we welcome you, Emmanuel!

2 Wonderful Counsellor, Mighty God,
Father for ever, the Prince of peace:
there'll be no end to your rule of justice,
for it shall increase.
Light of your face, come to pierce our darkness;
joy of your heart come to chase our gloom;
star of the morning, a new day dawning,
make our hearts your home.
    Worship the king . . .

3 Quietly he came as a helpless baby –
one day in power he will come again;
swift through the skies
        he will burst with splendour
on the earth to reign.
Jesus, I bow at your manger lowly:
now in my life let your will be done;
live in my flesh by your Spirit holy
till your Kingdom comes.
    Worship the king . . .

179 From Luke 2 (*The Song of Simeon / Nunc dimittis*)

Lord, now let your servant depart in peace,
according to your word:
for my eyes have seen your salvation,
which you have prepared
before the face of the people;
to be a light to lighten the Gentiles,
and to be the glory of your people Israel.

    Glory to the Father and to the Son
    and to the Holy Spirit,
    as it was in the beginning,
    is now, and shall be for ever,
    world without end. Amen.

180 From Luke 2 (*The Song of Simeon / Nunc dimittis*)
         J E Seddon (1915–1983)
         © Mrs Mavis Seddon / Jubilate Hymns

1 Lord, now let your servant
go his way in peace;
your great love has brought me
joy that will not cease:

2 For my eyes have seen him
promised from of old –
saviour of all people,
shepherd of one fold:

3 Light of revelation
to the gentiles shown,
light of Israel's glory
to the world made known.

181 © Angela Griffiths

1 Lord, speak softly to my soul;
tell me more of that first Christmas night
when a warm breath of peace
        covered Bethlehem,
and the hills came alive with your light.

2 Lord, speak slowly; draw me near,
let me share in the joy of your birth:
did you know, even then,
        you would bear my shame –
did you weep for the sins of this earth?

3 Lord, speak gently; lead me on,
guide me straight to that rough stable door;
let me gaze on that low, holy manger bed
where the royal Son of God slept on straw.

4 Lord, speak clearly, teach me now,
hear my prayer; let my love overflow:
then my anthem will rise on the pure clear air,
as I pledge back the life that I owe.

182 © Timothy Dudley-Smith †

1 Lord, who left the highest heaven
for a homeless human birth
and, a child within a stable,
came to share the life of earth –
    with your grace and mercy bless
    all who suffer homelessness.

2 Lord, who sought by cloak of darkness
refuge under foreign skies
from the swords of Herod's soldiers,
ravaged homes, and parents' cries –
    may your grace and mercy rest
    on the homeless and oppressed.

3 Lord, who lived secure and settled,
safe within the Father's plan,
and in wisdom, stature, favour
growing up from boy to man –
    with your grace and mercy bless
    all who strive for holiness.

4 Lord, who leaving home and kindred,
followed still as duty led,
sky the roof and earth the pillow
for the Prince of glory's head –
    with your grace and mercy bless
    sacrifice for righteousness.

5 Lord, who in your cross and passion
hung beneath a darkened sky,
yet whose thoughts were for your mother,
and a thief condemned to die –
    may your grace and mercy rest
    on the helpless and distressed.

6 Lord, who rose to life triumphant
with our whole salvation won,
risen, glorified, ascended,
all the Father's purpose done –
    may your grace, all conflict past,
    bring your children home at last.

4 When the heavens shall ring,
    and the choirs shall sing
at your coming to victory,
let your voice call me home
    saying, 'Yes, there is room!' –
there is room at your side for me.
    Then my heart shall rejoice, Lord Jesus,
    when you come and you call for me.

184
F Houghton (1874–1972)
© Overseas Missionary Fellowship †
and in this version Jubilate Hymns

1 Lord, you were rich beyond all splendour,
yet, for love's sake, became so poor;
leaving your throne in glad surrender,
sapphire-paved courts for stable floor:
    Lord, you were rich beyond all splendour,
    yet, for love's sake, became so poor.

2 You are our God beyond all praising,
yet, for love's sake, became a man
stooping so low, but sinners raising
heavenwards, by your eternal plan:
    You are our God beyond all praising,
    yet, for love's sake, became a man.

3 Lord, you are love beyond all telling,
Saviour and King, we worship you;
Emmanuel, within us dwelling,
make us and keep us pure and true:
    Lord, you are love beyond all telling,
    Saviour and King, we worship you.

185
© Christopher Porteous / Jubilate Hymns

1 Lowly Jesus, King of glory,
    born on earth a little child,
in your mother's arms a-sleeping,
    pure and gentle, undefiled:
how I long, Lord, to adore you,
    and to see you fast asleep,
like the shepherds round your manger,
    leaving hillside, leaving sheep!

2 Loving Jesus, be my Master,
    loving Jesus, be my King;
let me come close to your cradle,
    hear the good news angels bring:
peace, good-will, from God in heaven
    to all people here on earth,
through the coming of a baby,
    through his lowly stable-birth.

3 Precious Jesus, be my Saviour –
    in your mercy heal my sin;
please forgive me for my failures –
    may your Spirit enter in.
Gift of wonder, gift of glory,
    born to give us heavenly grace!
How I wish I were a wise man
    to behold you face to face!

183
E Elliott (1836–1897)
© in this version Word & Music / Jubilate Hymns

1 Lord, you left your throne
    and your kingly crown,
when you came to this earth for me,
but in Bethlehem's home
    there was found no room
for your holy nativity:
    O come to my heart, Lord Jesus;
    Emmanuel, come to me.

2 Heaven's arches rang when the angels sang,
proclaiming your royal degree,
but to lowly birth you came down on earth,
and in great humility:
    O come to my heart, Lord Jesus;
    Redeemer, be born in me.

3 You were sent, O Lord, with the living word
that should set your people free;
but with mocking scorn and with crown of thorn,
they bore you to Calvary:
    O come to my heart, Lord Jesus,
    your cross is my only plea.

4 Holy Jesus, my Redeemer
  in a manger for a bed,
  ox and ass may bow before you –
  but no pillow for your head.
  God's own Son who came to save me,
  let your Spirit rule my heart;
  let my body be your dwelling,
  and your love fill every part.

186
From 1 John 4
© Geoffrey Rand †

1 Love was born at Christmas
  in such a wondrous way,
  for humbly in a manger
  the Christ-child gently lay:
  love was deep within him –
    a love so filled with light,
  it shone in all its glory
    and made the whole world bright.

2 Let love be born this Christmas
  within my heart and mind,
  a love that knows no limits,
    a love that is divine:
  love is now within us
    to guide us on our way,
  for love was born at Christmas,
    God's love on Christmas Day.
  for love . . .

187/188
C Rossetti (1830–1894)
© in this version Jubilate Hymns

1 Love came down at Christmas,
  love all lovely, love divine;
  love was born at Christmas –
  star and angels gave the sign.

2 Worship we the Godhead,
  love incarnate, love divine;
  worship we our Jesus –
  what shall be our sacred sign?

3 Love shall be our token,
  love be yours and love be mine;
  love to God and neighbour,
  love for prayer and gift and sign.

189
After the Polish carol
© Michael Perry / Jubilate Hymns

1 Lullaby, little Jesus;
  there you lie, little Jesus –
    as the winds bite
    on this cold night –
  in the hay, little Jesus.
    As the winds bite
    on this cold night:
  Lullaby, little Jesus!

2 Lullaby, little Jesus;
  don't you cry, little Jesus:
    come tomorrow
    there'll be sorrow
  and dismay, little Jesus.
    Come tomorrow
    there'll be sorrow.
  Lullaby, little Jesus!

3 Lullaby, little Jesus:
  in the sky, little Jesus,
    there is singing,
    glory bringing
  to this day, little Jesus.
    There is singing,
    glory bringing.
  Lullaby, little Jesus!

190
After I Watts (1674–1748)
© in this version Michael Paget

1 Lullaby, baby, lie still and slumber;
  God's holy angels guard your bed,
  heavenly blessings without number
  gently falling round your head.
    Jesus descended from heaven to this world
    and he became a child for us all;
    God's Son descended
      from heaven to this world,
    and he became a child like you.

2 Cotton and silk are lining your cradle –
  not like the manger where our saviour lay;
  his chosen birthplace was a bare stable,
  and for his bedding, there was only some hay.
    Jesus descended . . .

3 May all our children know him and love him,
  trust and obey him all their days,
  then go and dwell for evermore with him,
  so they may see him and sing his praise.
    Jesus descended . . .

4 Lullaby, baby, be still and slumber;
  God's holy angels guard your bed,
  heavenly blessings, without number,
  gently falling round our head.
    Jesus descended . . .

191
© Paul Wigmore / Jubilate Hymns

1 Mary came with meekness,
    Jesus Christ to bear,
  laid the Lord of glory in a manger there.
    We come rejoicing,
    Jesus Christ to love:
    baby in a manger –
    king of heaven above!

2 Angels came with praises,
    Jesus Christ to name,
  heaven's choirs exalting
    him who bears our shame.
    We come rejoicing . . .

3 Shepherds came with trembling,
    Jesus Christ to see;
  king who, at their bidding,
    would their shepherd be.
    We come rejoicing . . .

4 Wise men came with treasure,
    Jesus Christ to bless –
  he who shares all blessings
    heaven and earth possess.
    We come rejoicing . . .

192

Mary and Joseph – praise with them:
  Jesus is born, Jesus is born;
worship this day in Bethlehem,
  Jesus is born, Jesus is born!

Angels have spoken – hear God's word,
  Peace on the earth, peace on the earth;
he who is born is Christ the Lord,
  peace on the earth, peace on the earth!

Shepherds have worshipped – join their song,
  Glory to God, glory to God;
this is the saviour promised long,
  glory to God, glory to God!

See the Creator – here he lies,
  God has come down, God has come down;
love has appeared before our eyes,
  God has come down, God has come down!

193

Mary had a baby, yes, Lord;
Mary had a baby, yes, my Lord;
Mary had a baby, yes, Lord;
  The people keep a-coming
  for to see her child!
  (OR: but the train has gone!)

QUESTION:
What did she name him?
  yes, Lord . . .

ANSWER:
Mary named him Jesus!
  yes, Lord . . .

QUESTION:
Where was he born?
  yes, Lord . . .

ANSWER:
Born in a stable!
  yes, Lord . . .

QUESTION:
Where did she lay him?
  yes, Lord . . .

ANSWER:
Laid him in a manger!
  yes, Lord . . .

194

Mary, listen to the angel of the Lord:
'Hail, O favoured one, the Lord is with you!
Do not be frightened, for he has chosen you;
you shall have a baby boy –
  let Jesus be his name.'
  He will be great
    and called the Son of the Most High,
  and will reign over Israel for ever:
  and of his kingdom there will be no end;
  and of his kingdom there will be no end.'

2 Mary answered, 'I am the servant of the Lord:
let it happen to me according to your word.
My soul sings out the greatness of the Lord;
he has done great things for me
  and holy is his name!'
  He will be great . . .

195/196

1 Mary sang a song, a song of love,
  magnified the mighty Lord above;
  melodies of praise his name extol
  from the very depths of Mary's soul:

2 'God the Lord has done great things for me,
  looked upon my life's humility;
  happy they shall call me from this day –
  merciful is he whom we obey.

3 'To the humble soul our God is kind,
  to the proud he brings unease of mind:
  who uplifts the poor, pulls down the strong?
  God alone has power to right the wrong!

4 'He who has been Israel's strength and stay
  fills the hungry, sends the rich away;
  he has shown his promise firm and sure,
  faithful to his people evermore.'

5 This was Mary's song as we recall,
  mother to the saviour of us all:
  magnify his name and sing his praise,
  worship and adore him, all your days!

197

1 Make way, make way,
  for Christ the king in splendour arrives;
  fling wide the gates
  and welcome him into your lives.
    Make way, make way,
    for the King of kings;
    make way, make way,
    and let his kingdom in!

2 He comes the broken hearts to heal,
  the prisoners to free;
  the deaf shall hear, the lame shall dance,
  the blind shall see.
    Make way . . .

3 And those who mourn with heavy hearts,
  who weep and sigh,
  with laughter, joy and royal crown
  he'll beautify.
    Make way . . .

4 We call you now to worship him
  as Lord of all,
  to have no gods before him –
  their thrones must fall!
    Make way . . .

198
Graham Kendrick
© Thankyou Music †

1 Meekness and majesty,
manhood and deity,
in perfect harmony –
the man who is God:
Lord of eternity
dwells in humanity,
kneels in humility
and washes our feet.
   Oh what a mystery –
   meekness and majesty:
   bow down and worship,
   for this is your God,
   this is your God!

2 Father's pure radiance,
perfect in innocence,
yet learns obedience
to death on a cross:
suffering to give us life,
conquering through sacrifice –
and, as they crucify,
prays, 'Father, forgive'.
   Oh what a mystery . . .

3 Wisdom unsearchable,
God the invisible,
love indestructible
in frailty appears:
Lord of infinity,
stooping so tenderly,
lifts our humanity
to the heights of his throne.
   Oh what a mystery . . .

199
Mavis Ford
© Springtide / Word Music (UK) †

Mighty in victory, glorious in majesty:
every eye shall see him when he appears,
coming in the clouds with power and glory.
   Hail to the king!
We must be ready, watching and praying,
serving each other, building his kingdom;
then every knee shall bow,
   then every tongue confess,
   Jesus is Lord!

200
Laura Winnen
© Celebration Services / Thankyou Music †

   My Lord, he is a coming soon –
   prepare the way of the Lord;
   get everything ready for that day,
   prepare the way of the Lord!

1 If you're asleep, it's time to wake up –
   awake, O sleeper, arise!
If you're in the dark, it's time to be lit –
   awake, O sleeper, arise!
   My Lord . . .

2 Come, Lord Jesus, come into my heart –
   prepare the way of the king!
He is coming, he's coming soon:
   prepare the way of the king!
   My Lord . . .

201
From Luke 1 (Song of Mary / Magnificat)
© Simon Humphreys

1 My soul glorifies the Lord,
and my spirit rejoices in my God, my saviour;
my soul glorifies the Lord,
and my spirit rejoices in his word:
for he has been mindful of his servant.
From now on,
all peoples will bless me,
for the mighty one has done great things for me
   Holy, holy, holy is the Lord;
   holy, holy, holy is the Lord.

2 His love extends to those who fear him,
from generation to generation;
His love extends to those who fear him –
praise his holy name:
he has brought down rulers from their thrones
but has uplifted the humble;
he has filled the hungry with good things,
and has sent the rich away empty.
   Holy, holy, holy . . .

202
Hilda M Day
© Anfield Music †
and in this version Word & Music / Jubilate Hymns

1 No room for the saviour at Bethlehem's inn,
   only a cattle shed;
no room on this earth for the dear Son of God,
   nowhere to lay his head.
Only a cross did they give to my Lord,
   only a borrowed tomb.
Today he is seeking a place in your heart –
   will you still say to him, 'No room'?

2 O Lord in my heart there's a welcome for you:
   gladly I now would say,
   'Come in, precious saviour;
      my heart and my life
   both shall be yours today.
Long have you waited and long knocked in vain
   outside my heart's closed door:
so cleanse me from sin, then, my Lord, enter in
   and live there for evermore!'

203
Tom Dowell
© Christian Fellowship of Columbia, Inc †

No weapon formed,
   or army or king,
shall be able to stand
   against the Lord and his Anointed;
no weapon formed . . .

All principalities and powers
   shall crumble before the Lord,
and our hearts shall be released,
and we shall return to the Lord.

204

From the French
W B Lindsay and Ruth Heller
© Blandford Press Ltd †

Now tell us, gentle Mary,
what did Gabriel say to you?
Now tell us of the tidings
that he brought to Galilee.
MARY:
He told me I was favoured,
that I would be the one
God chose to be the mother
of Jesus, his own son.

Now tell us, gentle Mary,
of the birth of Christ that morn;
now tell us of Christ Jesus,
where it was that he was born.
MARY:
Not in a palace glorious,
not in a silken bed,
but in a stable humble
did Jesus lay his head.

205

From Luke 1 (*The Song of Zechariah / Benedictus*)
© Michael Perry / Jubilate Hymns

O bless the God of Israel
    who comes to set us free;
who visits and redeems us,
    with love for all to see.
The prophets spoke of mercy,
    of rescue and release:
God shall fulfil his promise
    and bring our people peace.

He comes! the Child of David,
    the Son whom God has given;
he comes to live among us
    and raise us up to heaven:
before him goes his herald –
    forerunner in the way,
the prophet of salvation,
    the harbinger of Day.

Where once were fears and darkness,
    the sun begins to rise –
the dawning of forgiveness
    upon the sinner's eyes.
He guides the feet of pilgrims
    along the paths of peace:
O bless our God and Saviour,
    with songs that never cease!

206

After J F Wade (1711–1786)
F Oakeley (1802–1880) and others

O come, all ye faithful,
joyful and triumphant;
O come ye, O come ye to Bethlehem;
come and behold him,
        born the king of angels!
O come, let us adore him,
O come, let us adore him,
O come, let us adore him,
Christ the Lord!

2 God from God,
Light from light –
lo, he abhors not the virgin's womb!
Very God, begotten, not created.
    O come . . .

3 Sing, choirs of angels,
sing in exultation!
Sing, all ye citizens of heaven above,
'Glory to God in the highest!'
    O come . . .

4 Yea, Lord, we greet thee,
born for our salvation;
Jesus, to thee be glory given!
Word of the Father now in flesh appearing.
    O come . . .

OR, ON CHRISTMAS DAY:

4 Yea, Lord, we greet thee,
born this happy morning;
Jesus, to thee be glory given!
Word of the Father now in flesh appearing.
    O come . . .

207

From the Welsh
© Michael Perry / Jubilate Hymns

1 O come, Christians, wonder,
be thankful, and ponder
the birth of our saviour and Lord:
for we who were sighing,
and sinning, and dying,
in Jesus are fully restored.

2 So lift high your voices,
as heaven rejoices
to tell of the babe in the hay:
this Jesus – the holy,
the poor, and the lowly –
we praise him and serve him today!

3 Let sister and brother
speak peace to each other,
and brother and sister agree:
for love is our story –
to Jesus the glory
both now and for ever shall be.

208

Iain Anderson
© Springtide / Word Music (UK) †

O come, let us worship and bow down,
let us kneel before the Lord our king;
let us whisper his name – wonderful name –
    Jesus our Lord and king.

    O come, let us worship . . .

For he is Lord of all the earth,
his glory outshines the sun:
see him clothed in his robes of righteousness –
    God's belovèd Son.

    O come, let us worship . . .

209

From the Latin (thirteenth century)
J M Neale (1818–1866)
© in this version Jubilate Hymns

1 O come, O come, Emmanuel
and ransom captive Israel
who mourns in lonely exile here
until the Son of God draws near:
  Rejoice, rejoice!
  Emmanuel shall come to you, O Israel.

2 O come, true Branch of Jesse, free
your children from this tyranny;
from depths of hell your people save
to rise victorious from the grave:
  Rejoice, rejoice . . .

3 O come, bright Daybreak, come and cheer
our spirits by your advent here;
dispel the long night's lingering gloom
and pierce the shadows of the tomb:
  Rejoice, rejoice . . .

4 O come, strong Key of David, come
and open wide our heavenly home;
make safe the way that leads on high,
and close the path to misery:
  Rejoice, rejoice . . .

5 O come, O come, great Lord of might
who long ago on Sinai's height
gave all your tribes the ancient law,
in cloud and majesty and awe:
  Rejoice, rejoice . . .

210

From the German
© Paul Wigmore / Jubilate Hymns

1 O come all you children to Bethlehem town,
and see here a baby from heaven come down;
tread softly and enter on this sacred night
a stable with heavenly glory alight.

2 O come all you children, come here to the stall
and see here a child who is born Lord of all;
more fair than the angels in glory is he,
more lovely than cherubim ever could be.

3 O come all you children, and stand by his bed,
and see gentle Mary bend low at his head;
see Joseph, so humble in wondering joy,
kneel down at the feet of this most holy boy.

4 O come then you children,
    and hark at the throng
of angels, all crowding the sky with their song;
join in with their praises and joyfully sing
your loudest thanksgiving – for Jesus the King!

211

From Luke 1 (*Benedictus*)
© Michael Perry / Jubilate Hymns

1 O praise the Lord, the mighty God of Israel,
redeemer of his people he has come;
he raises up the dynasty of David
as promised by his prophets long ago.

2 Salvation from the hands of those who hate us!
His covenant with Abraham fulfilled!
He rescues us that, fearless,
    we might serve him
in honour and in goodness all our days.

3 And you will be the prophet of the Highest,
to go before him and prepare his way;
to give his people knowledge of salvation,
the blessing of forgiveness for their sins.

4 The Lord our God has shown his tender mercy
his shining sun will come to us from heaven
to dawn on those
    who live in death's dark shadow,
and guide our footsteps in the path of peace.

212

John Rutter
© Oxford University Press †
and in this version Word & Music / Jubilate Hymns

1 O leave your sheep,
where ewes with lambs are feeding;
you shepherds, hear
our message of good cheer.
No longer weep;
the angel tidings heeding,
to Bethlehem haste away
  Our Lord, our Lord,
  our Lord is born this happy day.
  Our Lord . . .

2 For Love lies there
within a lowly manger –
the infant poor
whom angel hosts adore!
Such perfect care
has saved us all from danger
and brought us to the fold.
  Now see, now see
  God's faithful love revealed of old.
  Now see . . .

3 You wise men three
arrayed in royal splendour,
true homage pay:
your king is born today!
The star you see
its radiance must surrender
before our Sun most bright.
  Your gifts. your gifts,
  your gifts are precious in his sight.
  Your gifts . . .

4 O Spirit blessed,
the source of life eternal,
our souls inspire
with your celestial fire!
We make our guest
the Christ, the Lord supernal,
and sing the peace on earth
  God gives, God gives,
  God gives us by this holy birth;
  God gives . . .

213-216 P Brooks (1835–1893)

O little town of Bethlehem,
how still we see you lie!
Above your deep and dreamless sleep
the silent stars go by:
yet in your dark streets shining
is everlasting light;
the hopes and fears of all the years
are met in you tonight.

For Christ is born of Mary
and, gathered all above
while mortals sleep, the angels keep
their watch of wondering love:
O morning stars, together
proclaim the holy birth,
and praises sing to God the king,
and peace to all the earth.

How silently, how silently
the wondrous gift is given!
So God imparts to human hearts
the blessings of his heaven:
no ear may hear his coming,
but in this world of sin,
where meek souls will receive him –
still the dear Christ enters in.

O holy child of Bethlehem,
descend to us we pray;
cast out our sin and enter in,
be born in us today!
We hear the Christmas angels
the great glad tidings tell –
O come to us, abide with us,
our Lord Emmanuel.

217 Michael Smith © Meadowgreen Music Company †

O Lord, our Lord,
how majestic is your name in all the earth;
O Lord, our Lord,
how majestic is your name in all the earth;
O Lord, we praise your name;
O Lord, we magnify your name.

Prince of peace, mighty God,
O Lord God almighty!

218 © Timothy Dudley-Smith †

O Prince of peace whose promised birth
the angels sang with 'Peace on earth,'
peace be to us and all beside,
    peace to us all –
peace to the world this Christmastide.

2 O Child who found to lay your head
no place but in a manger bed,
come where our doors stand open wide,
    peace to us all –
    peace to the world –
peace in our homes this Christmastide.

3 O Christ whom shepherds came to find,
their joy be ours in heart and mind;
let grief and care be laid aside,
    peace to us all –
    peace to the world –
    peace in our homes –
peace in our hearts this Christmastide.

4 O Saviour Christ, ascended Lord,
our risen Prince of life restored,
our Love who once for sinners died,
    peace to us all –
    peace to the world –
    peace in our homes –
    peace in our hearts –
peace with our God this Christmastide!

219 J S B Monsell (1811–1875)

1 O worship the Lord in the beauty of holiness,
bow down before him, his glory proclaim;
with gold of obedience
        and incense of lowliness,
kneel and adore him – the Lord is his name.

2 Low at his feet lay your burden of carefulness,
high on his heart he will bear it for you,
comfort your sorrows
        and answer your prayerfulness,
guiding your steps in the way that is true.

3 Fear not to enter his courts in the slenderness
of the poor wealth
        you would count as your own;
truth in its beauty and love in its tenderness –
these are the offerings to bring to his throne.

4 These, though we bring them
        in trembling and fearfulness,
he will accept for the name that is dear;
mornings of joy give
        for evenings of tearfulness,
trust for our trembling and hope for our fear.

5 O worship the Lord in the beauty of holiness,
bow down before him his glory proclaim;
with gold of obedience
        and incense of lowliness,
kneel and adore him – the Lord is his name.

220 © Pete Ratcliffe / Jubilate Hymns

1 Off to David's town they go,
hurrying down the Bethlehem road,
shepherds run eagerly to seek out
        the new-born king.
Stumbling on cheerfully through the cold night,
travelling on closer to Bethlehem's light,
thankful to Gabriel who told them the news,
that a king was born today.
    Angels sang, steeples rang, shepherds ran
    to welcome Jesus,
        holy boy – brought their joy
    all for Jesus the king who's born today.

2 How will they find the baby there –
lots of different places in Bethlehem?
No need to fear –
 the angel gave them a holy sign:
'Search for a manger,' the angel said,
'there in a stable he'll lay his head!'
Only a cattle shed with manger for Jesus,
the king who's born today!
 Angels sang, steeples rang, shepherds ran
to welcome Jesus,
  holy boy – brought their joy
all for Jesus the king who's born today.

221
Dave Bilbrough
© Thankyou Music †

Oh, the valleys shall ring
with the sound of praise,
and the lion shall lie with the lamb;
of his government there shall be no end
and his glory shall fill the earth.
May your will be done,
may your kingdom come –
let it rule, let it reign in our lives.
There's a shout in the camp
  as we answer the call:
hail the king, hail the Lord of lords!

222
© Mary Chandler

1 Oh where do you think baby Jesus was born,
on that first Christmas night long ago?
Was he born in a house all cosy and warm
on that first Christmas night long ago?
 No, no! No, no!
Oh where do you think he was born?

2 Now Mary and Joseph had travelled so far
on that first Christmas night long ago;
they went to an inn
  and they knocked on the door
on that first Christmas night long ago.
 'No room! No room!'
the innkeeper said, 'There's no room!'

3 So where do you think baby Jesus was born,
on that first Christmas night long ago?
He was born in a stable so cold and so bare
on that first Christmas night long ago.
 Yes, yes! Yes, yes!
in a stable – a manger his bed.

4 So where do you think baby Jesus was born,
on that first Christmas night long ago?
He was God's only Son,
  and he came down to earth
on that first Christmas night long ago:
 for me, for you –
he was born to give life to us all!

223
From Matthew 2
Margaret Clarkson
© Hope Publishing Company †

1 Over desert, hill and valley,
come from lands afar,
moved the wondering Magi westward
led by lustrous star.
Whence it came or where it led them
not for them to know;
only theirs in faith to journey
where it bade them go.

2 On they went through starlit midnights,
following till it led
where the Prince of kings lay sleeping
in his humble bed.
Offering him their gifts, they worshipped
where the saviour lay;
then, to their own land returning,
went another way.

3 When we've seen his star of promise
shining through earth's night,
when we've followed till we've found him,
Love's eternal Light,
paths of sin no more allure us
from that hallowed day:
souls who once have seen their Saviour
walk his holy way.

224
© Michael Perry / Jubilate Hymns

1 On a night when the world
 in its sin and sorrow lay,
the saviour Jesus was born.

2 On a night when the world
 in its sin and sorrow lay,
close in a stall,
there the saviour Jesus was born.

3 On a night when the world
 in its sin and sorrow lay,
in Bethlehem,
close in a stall,
there the saviour Jesus was born.

4 On a night when the world
 in its sin and sorrow lay,
on Christmas Day,
in Bethlehem,
close in a stall,
there the saviour Jesus was born.

5 On a night when the world
 in its sin and sorrow lay,
'Peace on earth!' –
on Christmas Day,
in Bethlehem,
close in a stall,
there the saviour Jesus was born.

On a night when the world
in its sin and sorrow lay,
angels were singing,
'Peace on the earth!' –
on Christmas Day,
in Bethlehem,
close in a stall,
there the saviour Jesus was born.

On a night when the world
in its sin and sorrow lay,
heavens were blazing,
angels were singing,
'Peace on the earth!' –
on Christmas Day,
in Bethlehem,
close in a stall,
there the saviour Jesus was born.

On a night when the world
in its sin and sorrow lay,
shepherds were watching,
heavens were blazing,
angels were singing,
'Peace on the earth!' –
on Christmas Day,
in Bethlehem,
close in a stall,
there the saviour Jesus was born.

On a night when the world
in its sin and sorrow lay,
sheep were reclining,
shepherds were watching,
heavens were blazing,
angels were singing,
'Peace on the earth!' –
on Christmas Day,
in Bethlehem,
close in a stall,
there the saviour Jesus was born.

0 On a night when the world
in its sin and sorrow lay,
people were sleeping,
sheep were reclining,
shepherds were watching,
heavens were blazing,
angels were singing,
'Peace on the earth!' –
on Christmas Day,
in Bethlehem,
close in a stall,
there the saviour Jesus was born.

1 On a night when the world
in its sin and sorrow lay,
bright skies were shining,
people were sleeping,
sheep were reclining,
shepherds were watching,
heavens were blazing,
angels were singing,

'Peace on the earth!' –
on Christmas Day,
in Bethlehem,
close in a stall,
there the saviour Jesus was born.

12 On a night when the world
in its sin and sorrow lay,
wise men were riding,
bright skies were shining,
people were sleeping,
sheep were reclining,
shepherds were watching,
heavens were blazing,
angels were singing,
'Peace on the earth!' –
on Christmas Day,
in Bethlehem,
close in a stall,
there the saviour Jesus was born.

225 © Paul Wigmore / Jubilate Hymns

Oh what a day for singing –
bells in Bethlehem are ringing;
Oh what a day for singing
Christmas joy to all the world:
so, sing songs of celebration,
ring out bells of jubilation,
for Jesus Christ the Lord
has come to be our king
on this Christmas day!

1 Our God was able
to come down on earth,
born in a stable
to bring us new birth;
angels were praising
as shepherds were gazing
on Jesus, the Son of God.
Oh what a day . . .

2 Wise men were riding –
through deserts they came,
star for their guiding
and king for their aim;
coming before him
they knelt to adore him
with incense and gold and myrrh.
Oh what a day . . .

226
After C Coffin (1676–1749)
J Chandler (1806–1876)
© in this version Word & Music / Jubilate Hymns

1 On Jordan's bank the Baptist's cry
announces that the Lord is nigh:
awake and listen for he brings
glad tidings of the King of kings.

2 Let every heart be cleansed from sin,
   make straight the way for God within,
   and so prepare to be the home
   where such a mighty guest may come.

3 For you are our salvation, Lord,
   our refuge and our great reward;
   without your grace we waste away
   like flowers that wither and decay.

4 To heal the sick, stretch out your hand,
   and make the fallen sinner stand;
   shine out, and let your light restore
   earth's own true loveliness once more.

5 To you, O Christ, all praises be,
   whose advent sets your people free;
   whom with the Father we adore
   and Holy Spirit evermore!

227 © Elizabeth Cosnett

1 On this very special night
   noise is hushed and stars are bright;
   from the huge and shining sky
   angel songs come drifting by.
     On the earth and in the sky
     glory be to God on high!
     On the earth . . .

2 Presents glitter on the tree,
   gifts for him or her or me;
   but we find the best of all
   hidden in a cattle stall.
     God has given to us all
     Mary's baby in the stall.
     God has given . . .

3 Shepherds are the first to see
   Jesus and his family;
   news from God has come to them
   'Go at once to Bethlehem!'
     God is very close to them
     all the way to Bethlehem.
     God is very . . .

4 Jesus in the cattle shed
   doesn't have a proper bed;
   donkey gives a loud hee-haw,
   'You may share my yellow straw.
     Welcome little friend, hee-haw!
     Welcome to my yellow straw!
     Welcome, little friend . . .

5 Stars and angels fade away,
   sunrise comes on Christmas Day;
   child and mother still are there,
   safe in Joseph's loving care.
     Tell the story everywhere!
     Here is joy for all to share!
     Tell the story . . .

6 Jesus Christ is here to stay!
   Kings arrive from far away.
   Incense, gold and myrrh they bring,
   presents fit for any king.
     All their very best they bring
     for the love of Christ, their king
     All their very best . . .

228 C F Alexander (1818–1895)

1 Once in royal David's city
   stood a lowly cattle shed,
   where a mother laid her baby
   in a manger for his bed:
   Mary was that mother mild,
   Jesus Christ, her little child.

2 He came down to earth from heaven
   who is God and Lord of all;
   and his shelter was a stable
   and his cradle was a stall:
   with the poor and meek and lowly
   lived on earth our saviour holy.

3 And through all his wondrous childhood
   he would honour and obey,
   love and watch the gentle mother
   in whose tender arms he lay:
   Christian children all should be
   kind, obedient, good as he.

4 For he is our childhood's pattern:
   day by day like us he grew;
   he was little, weak and helpless –
   tears and smiles like us he knew:
   and he feels for all our sadness,
   and he shares in all our gladness.

5 And our eyes at last shall see him,
   through his own redeeming love;
   for that child, so dear and gentle,
   is our Lord in heaven above:
   and he leads his children on
   to the place where he has gone.

6 Not in that poor lowly stable
   with the oxen standing by,
   we shall see him, but in heaven,
   set at God's right hand on high:
   there his children gather round
   bright like stars, with glory crowned.

229 From Luke 1 (The Song of Zechariah / Benedictus)
© Timothy Dudley-Smith †

1 Our God has turned to his people,
   he has saved them and set them free
   and raised up a mighty Saviour
   who has given them victory –
   a King in the house of David
   as his holy prophets foretold!
   Our God has redeemed his people
   as he promised in days of old.

2 Our God has stooped to redeem us
   in a covenant ages long,
   from all who would seek to hurt us,
   from the hands of malice and wrong:
   the oath he swore to our fathers,
   that, delivered and free from fears,
   we serve with a holy worship
   in his presence for all our years.

3 And you, O Child, are the prophet,
   the forerunner of God most high,
   to show how in tender mercy
   he will put our offences by.
   The day shall dawn on our darkness
   and the light of heaven increase,
   to guide our feet from the shadows
   that we walk in the path of peace.

230
Graham Kendrick
© Thankyou Music †

1 One shall tell another,
   and he shall tell his friend;
   husbands, wives and children
   shall come following on.
   From house to house in families
   shall more be gathered in;
   and lights will shine in every street,
   so warm and welcoming.
     Come on in and taste the new wine,
     the wine of the kingdom,
     the wine of the kingdom of God:
     here is healing and forgiveness,
     the wine of the kingdom,
     the wine of the kingdom of God.

2 Compassion of the Father
   is ready now to flow;
   through acts of love and mercy
   we must let it show.
   He turns now from his anger
   to show a smiling face,
   and longs that we should stand beneath
   the fountain of his grace.
     Come on in . . .

3 He longs to do much more than
   our faith has yet allowed,
   to thrill us and surprise us
   with his sovereign power.
   Where darkness has been darkest,
   the brightest light will shine;
   his invitation comes to us –
   it's yours and it is mine.
     Come on in . . .

231
From Isaiah 62, © NIV, adapted †
© Pete Lawry / Music for the King †

   Pass through, pass through the gates;
   prepare the way for the people.
   Build up, build up the road;
   remove the stones,
   raise a banner for the nations!

1 I have posted watchmen on your walls,
     O Jerusalem,
   they will never be silent:
   you who call on the Lord, give yourselves
   and give him also no rest
   till he establishes Jerusalem,
   and makes her the praise of the earth!
     Pass through . . .

2 I declare you will be called the Holy People,
   the Redeemed of the Lord;
   you will be called the Loved One, Sought After,
   the City No Longer Laid Waste,
   when he establishes Jerusalem,
   and makes her the praise of the earth!
     Pass through . . .

232
From Isaiah 9
Mark Cheesman and Chris Jeffrey
© Mustard Seed Music †

1 People walking in the dark,
   people living in a land of shadows –
   now their darkness is dispelled,
   for a light has dawned.

2 Unto us a child is born,
   unto us a son is given,
   and the government is his,
   and he is called:
     Wonderful Counsellor, Mighty God,
     Everlasting Father, Prince of peace;
     Wonderful . . .

3 He will reign for ever,
   his peace will never end;
   he will bring us joy,
   will bring us life, our freedom defend.

INSTRUMENTAL BREAK

4 Unto us a child is born,
   unto us a son is given,
   and the government is his,
   and he is called:
     Wonderful Counsellor, Mighty God,
     Everlasting Father, Prince of peace;
     Wonderful Counsellor, Mighty God,
     Everlasting Father,
     Prince of, Prince of peace!

233
© Judy Davies / Jubilate Hymns

     Play your pipe, bang your drum,
     sing to Christ the Saviour;
     come and worship, come and worship,
     worship Christ our king!

1 Shepherds come a-dancing,
   bring your pipe and drum;
   come and see the baby –
   run, run, run!
     Play your pipe . . .

2 Peaceful in the manger
   see him lying there;
   gently gather round him –
   Oh take care!
     Play your pipe . . .

3 Listen to the angels,
   can you hear them sing –
   welcoming the saviour?
   He's our king!
      Play your pipe, bang your drum,
      sing to Christ the Saviour;
      come and worship, come and worship,
      worship Christ our king!

234
From Isaiah 12
© Christopher Idle / Jubilate Hymns

   Praise God today:
   his glories never end;
   our judge becomes in Christ
   our greatest friend.

1 God brings us comfort
      where his anger burned,
   so judgement and fear
      to peace and trust are turned.
   Praise God today:
   his mercies never end;
   our judge becomes in Christ
   our greatest friend.

2 Wells of salvation
      streams of life will bring;
   with joy we shall draw
      from this refreshing spring.
   Praise God today:
   his blessings never end;
   our judge becomes in Christ
   our greatest friend.

3 Songs shall be his
      for this victorious day:
   give thanks to his name,
      and teach the earth to say,
   Praise God today:
   his triumphs never end;
   our judge becomes in Christ
   our greatest friend.

4 Love lives among us,
      Israel's holy One
   who comes to the rescue –
      see what God has done!
   Praise God today:
   his wonders never end;
   our judge becomes in Christ
   our greatest friend.

235
© Brian Black and Word & Music /
Jubilate Hymns

1 Praise for coming of the King,
   praise for song the angels sing,
   praise for gifts the wise men bring,
   praise for Christmas – ring bells, ring!

2 Praise for shining star on high,
   praise for humble shepherds nigh,
   praise for baby Jesus' cry,
   'Praise for Christmas!' – hearts reply.

3 Praise for gift of God's own Son,
   praise for victory he has won,
   praise while timeless ages run,
   praise for Christmas – praise be done!

4 Praise for Christmas – all our days,
   heart and soul and voice shall raise
   love for God in all his ways,
   praise for Christmas – sound his praise!

   Sound his praise;
   sound his praise!

236
F van Alstyne (1820–1915)
© in this version Word & Music / Jubilate Hymns

1 Praise him, praise him –
      Jesus, our mighty redeemer;
   sing, O earth,
      his wonderful love proclaim:
   hail him, hail him,
      highest archangels in glory;
   strength and honour
      give to his holy name!
   Like a shepherd,
      Jesus will guard his children,
   in his arms
      he'll carry them all day long.
   Praise him, praise him,
   tell of his excellent greatness;
   praise him, praise him
   ever in joyful song!

2 Praise him, praise him –
      Jesus, our mighty redeemer;
   for our sins he suffered,
      and bled, and died:
   he – our rock,
      our hope of eternal salvation –
   hail him, hail him,
      Jesus, the crucified!
   Sound his praises –
      Jesus who bore our sorrows:
   love unbounded,
      wonderful, deep, and strong.
   Praise him, praise him . . .

3 Praise him, praise him –
      Jesus, our mighty redeemer;
   heavenly arches,
      loud with hosannas ring!
   Jesus, Saviour,
      reigning for ever and ever:
   crown him, crown him,
      prophet and priest and king!
   Christ is coming,
      over the world victorious;
   power and glory
      now to the Lord belong:
   Praise him, praise him . . .

237
From Luke 2
© Christopher Idle / Jubilate Hymns

1 Praise to God and peace on earth!
   hear what heaven's angels say;
   fear shall die at glory's birth –
   *Jesus is alive today!

2 Shepherds have no time to lose,
come to worship, go their way
bursting with the latest news –
*Jesus is alive today!

3 Mary wonders at her child,
keeps in mind as well she may
promises in him fulfilled –
*Jesus is alive today!

4 Angels' music, shepherds' word,
we shall sing as well as they;
Mary's Son is Christ the Lord –
*Jesus is alive today!

* On Christmas Day may be sung:
Jesus Christ is born today!

238
From Colossians 1
© Christopher Idle / Jubilate Hymns

1 Praise to God the Father!
he who saves his people,
rescues us from darkest powers
and tyrannies of night,
brings us liberation
by his Son, Christ Jesus,
who bears the likeness
of immortal light.

2 Forces seen and unseen
made in the beginning,
depths of spirit, heights of mind,
and worlds in time and space:
all in Christ created,
by and through and for him,
in Christ existing
find in him their place.

3 Origin and Firstborn
of the church, his body,
raised from death to be its Head
in sovereignty alone:
God's full nature sharing,
universe-reclaiming,
peacemaking Saviour –
praise to Christ the Son!

239
Graham Kendrick
Thankyou Music †

1 Praise to our God
who alone is the mighty One robed in majesty!
Come and bow down,
worship and adore.

2 Bring to him now,
as an offering of fragrance sweet,
all the prayers of your heart to his throne;
with thanksgiving, come!

The Lord Almighty –
his love endures for ever,
his grace and mercy ever sure;
his power will never, never
fail or falter,
or his love grow cold.

The Lord Almighty . . .

240
From Luke 1 (*The Song of Zechariah / Benedictus*)
Elaine Davies
© Mustard Seed Music †

1 Praise to the mighty Lord of all,
the God of Israel;
he has redeemed his people
for he is sending us a saviour.
And through him his word will be fulfilled;
yes, through him his word will be fulfilled.

2 Someone to save his people
from hatred and scorn:
the holy prophets foretold of the One
who protects us from our enemies.
And through him . . .

3 And with the Lord our saviour,
the one yet to come,
we'll be made holy and acceptable
for serving the Lord our God.
And through him . . .

4 Heaven's dawn is soon to break,
and people in the darkness
shall see the light of the holy One
leading his people to the path of peace.
And through him . . .

241
From Isaiah 40
Pip and Alison Rosedale
© Restoration Music Ltd †

1 Prepare the way for Jesus to return,
in the desert make a highway;
through the wilderness make
straight the way for him,
where streams of living water may flow.
We'll make highway for the Lord,
we'll make highway for King Jesus;
we'll make highway
for the Bridegroom to come.
We'll make highway for the Lord,
we'll make highway for King Jesus;
we'll make highway
for the Bridegroom to return.

2 Every valley shall be raised up,
every mountain, hill, brought low;
and all the rough ground shall be made smooth,
and the rugged places a plain.
We'll make a highway . . .

3 And the glory of the Lord shall be revealed,
as he purifies our lives;
and the whole wide world
shall see the bride prepared,
as the darkness comes to the light.
We'll make a highway . . .

242
Mary Smail
© Renewal Servicing †

1 Prepare the way of the Lord,
make his paths straight;
open the gates
that he may enter freely into our lives.
Hosanna! we cry to the Lord.

And we will fill the earth
with the sound of his praise:
Jesus is Lord – let him be adored!
Yes, we will have this man to reign over us,
hosanna – we follow the Lord!

2 And he will come to us as he came before,
clothed in his glory, to stand in our place;
and we behold him, now
our priest, Lord and king.
Hosanna! we sing to the Lord.
And we will . . .

3 Prepare the way of the Lord,
make his paths straight;
open the gates
that he may enter freely into our lives.
Hosanna! we cry to the Lord.
And we will . . .

243
Susie Killen and Anne Johnson
© Ears and Eyes Music †

Prepare the way, the way for the Lord,
make straight the highway for our God.
Do you not know? Have you not heard?
He left the throne to come to his own
to redeem them.

1 The Word, through whom all things
were created,
brought light, light that gives life to us all,
became flesh and lived for a while among us,
revealed his glory,
the glory of the one, true God.
Prepare the way . . .

2 The Light has never been extinguished,
though darkness bruised it with its evil sin;
grace and truth and righteousness
have triumphed:
freed from our sin
we worship him who reigns forever.
Prepare the way . . .

244
Traditional
© in this version Word & Music / Jubilate Hymns

1 Rejoice and be merry in songs and in mirth;
O praise our redeemer, all mortals on earth!
for this is the birthday of Jesus our king,
who brought us salvation –
his praises we'll sing!

2 A heavenly vision appeared in the sky;
vast numbers of angels the shepherds did spy,
proclaiming the birthday of Jesus our king,
who brought us salvation –
his praises we'll sing!

3 And soon in the sky a bright star did appear,
which led the wise men from the east
to draw near;
they found the messiah, Christ Jesus our king,
who brought us salvation –
his praises we'll sing!

4 They came and they offered
myrrh, incense and gold –
for God's gracious purpose
these treasures foretold:
then worshipped for ever be Jesus our king,
who brought us salvation –
his praises we'll sing!

245
From the Latin
© Michael Perry / Jubilate Hymns

Rejoice with heart and voice!
now is our Saviour
of the virgin Mary born –
so rejoice!

1 At this time our God fulfils
all our expectation:
let us offer hearts and wills
in rededication.
Rejoice . . .

2 God of God when time began,
Lord of all creation:
we revere the Son of Man
at his incarnation.
Rejoice . . .

3 Alleluia! Let us sing
hymns of adoration,
blessing Christ our worthy king
in this celebration!
Rejoice . . .

246
Frank Hernandez
© Sparrow Song / Cherry Lane Music Ltd †

1 Rejoice, rejoice,
a saviour has come:
to God be glory!
We hail his birth
with 'Peace on earth!'
for Christ the Lord is he.
Wonderful Counsellor, Mighty God –
this shall be his name;
Eternal Father, Prince of peace –
with justice he shall reign!

2 Rejoice, rejoice,
a virgin was born
a child most marvellous!
The scriptures tell
Emmanuel
means 'God is with us'.
Wonderful, Counsellor . . .

3 Rejoice, rejoice, for he will save
his people from their sins;
and he shall bless
with righteousness
the one who trusts in him.
Wonderful, Counsellor . . .

4 And he shall be great, he shall be great,
and there shall be no end to his kingdom;
and he shall reign for evermore:
Jesus Christ the Lord!

247

Graham Kendrick
© Thankyou Music †

Rejoice, rejoice! Christ is in you –
the hope of glory in our hearts.
He lives, he lives!
his breath is in you.
Arise! A mighty army we arise!

1 Now is the time for us to march upon the land –
into our hands he will give the ground we claim;
he rides in majesty to lead us into victory,
the world shall see that Christ is Lord.
Rejoice . . .

2 God is at work in us his purpose to perform –
building a kingdom of power not of words;
where things impossible
by faith shall be made possible:
let's give the glory to him now.
Rejoice . . .

3 Though we are weak,
his grace is everything we need –
we're made of clay, but this treasure is within;
he turns our weaknesses into his opportunities,
so that the glory goes to him.
Rejoice . . .

248

From Matthew 1 and Luke 2
Stuart Dauermann
© Lillenas Publishing Company / Thankyou Music †

Rejoice, rejoice,
for king Messiah's born in Bethlehem;
rejoice, the Son of David's come!
Rejoice, rejoice . . .

1 'Where is the One
who's born the king Emmanuel,
for we have come with frankincense to Israel?'
The eastern star of Bethlehem
has led us here to worship him.
O sons of men:
Rejoice, rejoice . . .

2 My eyes have seen the day of your salvation,
fulfilment of your word of revelation,
a light to lighten Gentiles well,
and glory for God's Israel –
of him they tell.
Rejoice, rejoice . . .

249

Graham Kendrick and Chris Rolinson
© Thankyou Music †

1 Restore, O Lord,
the honour of your name
in works of sovereign power;
come shake the earth again
that all may see,
and come with reverent fears
to the living God
whose Kingdom shall outlast the years.

2 Restore, O Lord,
in all the earth your fame,
and in our time revive
the Church that bears your name;
and in your anger,
Lord, remember mercy –
O living God,
whose mercy shall outlast the years.

3 Bend us, O Lord,
where we are hard and cold,
in your refiner's fire;
come purify the gold:
though suffering comes,
and evil crouches near,
still our living God
is reigning – he is reigning here!

4 Restore, O Lord,
the honour of your name
in works of sovereign power;
come shake the earth again
that all may see,
and come with reverent fears
to the living God
whose Kingdom shall outlast the years.

250

© Pete Ratcliffe / Jubilate Hymns

1 Riding out across the desert,
travelling over sandy plains,
comes a company of wise men,
moving steadily along their way;
leaving all their friends behind them,
guided by the star so bright,
now they've got to keep on going –
must not let the star get out of sight.
Riding through the desert,
gently the wise men go,
onwards to the king
who was promised long ago;
but they don't know
where they're going to find him –
there's many towns to search –
so they'll keep on following the star,
for it will lead them to his place of birth.

2 Wise men on their desert journey,
travelled many miles so far –
though they're getting tired and weary,
town of Bethlehem is not too far:
how they long to worship Jesus
and honour him with royal gifts –
hearts are full of joy and wonder
as they're searching for the new born king!
Riding through the desert . . .

251

© Michael Perry / Jubilate Hymns

Ring out the bells –
the joyful news is breaking;
ring out the bells
for Jesus Christ is born!

1 Angels in wonder
      sing of his glory;
   shepherds returning
      tell us the story.
   Ring out the bells –
   the joyful news is breaking;
   ring out the bells
   for Jesus Christ is born!

2 Let all creation
      worship before him:
   earth bring him homage,
      heaven adore him!
   Ring out . . .

3 Prophets have spoken –
      hark to their warning:
   shadows are passing,
      soon comes the morning!
   Ring out . . .

252 © Michael Perry / Jubilate Hymns

1 Ring, bells of Bethlehem,
      ding-dong-ding, ding-a-dong-a-ding;
   rise up, Jerusalem,
   joyfully sing.
   Come from your lands afar,
      ding-dong-ding, ding-a-dong-a-ding,
   follow the royal star,
   look for the king!

2 Come, as the wise of old,
      ding-dong-ding, ding-a-dong-a-ding;
   frankincense, myrrh and gold
   joyfully bring:
   incense shows willing prayers,
      ding-dong-ding, ding-a-dong-a-ding,
   myrrh his great love declares,
   gold marks him king!

3 Ring, bells of Bethlehem,
      ding-dong-ding, ding-a-dong-a-ding;
   rise up, Jerusalem,
   joyfully sing.
   Come and before him bow,
      ding-dong-ding, ding-a-dong-a-ding,
   open your treasures now,
   welcome your king!

253 Harry Bollbach
© Singspiration Music /
Universal Songs B.V. / Cherry Pie Music †

1 Ring the bells, ring the bells,
   let the whole world know
   Christ was born in Bethlehem
   many years ago:

2 Born to die that we might live,
   came to earth new life to give;
   born of Mary, born so low,
   many years ago.

3 God the Father gave his Son –
   gave his own belovèd One
   to this wicked, sinful earth,
   to bring mankind his love – new birth!

4 Ring the bells, ring the bells,
   let the whole world know
   Christ the saviour lives today,
   as he did so long ago.

254 © Barbara McArthur †

1 Royal sons of a royal king,
   made to worship, made to praise –
   kings and priests to the King of kings,
   made to worship him.

2 Lord, we offer royal praise –
   gold and frankincense and myrrh;
   Lord, we come in holiness,
   Lord, we worship you.

255 Frances Norton
© Boosey & Hawkes Music Publisher Ltd †

1 Sent away to a cattle shed!
   Can you imagine our Lord's sweet head
   laid to rest on a pillow of straw?
      Candles and crowns and cribs
      were there none,
      only Mary and Joseph
      and the stars above.

2 Born in a manger while oxen fed –
   can you imagine our sweet saviour's head
   was laid on a blanket of straw and hay?
      Candles and crowns . . .

3 But what sweet sense in our saviour's birth –
   the lessons all there for us to learn,
   no need for trumpets, jewels or crowns!
      Candles and crowns . . .

256 E Caswall (1814–1878)
© in this version Jubilate Hymns

1 See, amid the winter snow,
   born for us on earth below;
   see, the gentle Lamb appears,
   promised from eternal years:
      Hail, O ever-blessèd morn;
      hail, redemption's happy dawn!
      Sing through all Jerusalem:
      'Christ is born in Bethlehem!'

2 Low within a manger lies
   he who built the starry skies;
   he who, throned in height sublime,
   reigns above the cherubim:
      Hail, O ever-blessèd morn . . .

3 TREBLE VOICES
   Say, you humble shepherds, say
   what your joyful news today?
   Tell us why you left your sheep
   on the lonely mountain steep:
      Hail, O ever-blessèd morn . . .

4 MEN
   'As we watched at dead of night,
   all around us shone a light;
   angels singing Peace on earth
   told us of a Saviour's birth.'
      Hail, O ever-blessèd morn . . .

5 Sacred infant, king most dear,
   what a tender love was here,
   thus to come from highest bliss
   down to such a world as this!
     Hail, O ever-blessèd morn . . .

6 Holy Saviour, born on earth,
   teach us by your lowly birth;
   grant that we may ever be
   taught by such humility.
     Hail, O ever-blessèd morn . . .

257 © Michael Perry / Jubilate Hymns

1 See him lying on a bed of straw:
   a draughty stable with an open door;
   Mary cradling the babe she bore –
   the prince of glory is his name.
     O now carry me to Bethlehem
     to see the Lord appear to men –
     just as poor as was the stable then,
     the prince of glory when he came.

2 Star of silver sweep across the skies,
   show where Jesus in the manger lies;
   shepherds, swiftly from your stupor rise
   to see the saviour of the world!
     O now carry . . .

3 Angels, sing again the song you sang,
   bring God's glory to the heart of man;
   sing that Bethl'em's little baby can
   be salvation to the soul.
     O now carry . . .

4 Mine are riches, from your poverty,
   from your innocence, eternity;
   mine forgiveness by your death for me,
   child of sorrow for my joy.
     O now carry . . .

258 © Stanley Johnson

1 See the dawn appearing, lighting the sky –
   though shadows fly, don't you awake!
   The daylight breaking shines bright and clear –
   though day is near, don't you awake.
   Angels have sung you their lullabies –
   capture this moment before it dies.
     See the dawn appearing
     lighting the sky –
     though shadows fly,
     don't you awake!

2 Ox and ass are stirring – though they draw near
   no need to fear, don't you awake.
   Though shepherds greet you kneeling to pray,
   king born today, don't you awake.
   Wise men will bring you their gifts of gold,
   born to be king as the prophets told.
     See the dawn appearing . . .

3 Cruel day awaits you, dawn's icy breath,
   sorrow and death, when you awake.
   Rough hands will seize you –
     scorned and denied,
   nailed, crucified when you awake.
   Though people hail you today as king,
     they will not hear the Good News you bring.
       See the dawn appearing . . .

259 © Timothy Dudley-Smith †

1 See, to us a child is born –
   glory breaks on Christmas morn!
   Now to us a Son is given –
   praise to God in highest heaven!

2 On his shoulder rule shall rest –
   in him all the earth be blessed!
   Wise and wonderful his Name –
   heaven's Lord in human frame!

3 Mighty God, who mercy brings –
   Lord of lords and King of kings!
   Father of eternal days –
   every creature sing his praise!

4 Everlasting Prince of peace –
   truth and righteousness increase!
   He shall reign from shore to shore –
   Christ is King for evermore!

Lines 1 and 3: choir or solo
Lines 2 and 4: all

260 From *Quem pastores laudavere* (fifteenth century)
G B Caird (1917–1984)
© Mrs V M Caird

1 Shepherds came their praises bringing,
   who had heard the angels singing:
   'Far from you be fear unruly,
   Christ is king of glory born.'

2 Wise men whom a star had guided
   incense, gold, and myrrh provided,
   made their sacrifices truly
   to the king of glory born.

3 Jesus born the king of heaven,
   Christ to us through Mary given,
   to your praise and honour duly
   be resounding glory done.

261 © Paul Wigmore / Jubilate Hymns

1 Small wonder the star,
     small wonder the light,
   the angels in chorus,
     the shepherds in fright;
   but stable and manger for God –
   no small wonder!

2 Small wonder the kings,
     small wonder they bore
   the gold and incense,
     the myrrh, to adore;
   but God gives his life on a cross –
   no small wonder!

3 Small wonder the love,
      small wonder the grace,
   the power, the glory,
      the light of his face;
   but all to redeem my poor heart –
   no small wonder!

262
© Peter Brown. In this version
Word & Music / Jubilate Hymns

1 Shepherds, leave your drowsy sheep,
   shepherds, see the babe asleep:
   see him in a stable.
      He's the Lord of creation
      come down from heaven –
      such is his love.

2 Angels, sing your song of praise,
   angels, on this day of days,
   praise him as you're able.
      He's the Lord of creation . . .

3 Nations, * leave your cares behind,
   nations, come, your Lord to find –
   Jesus is no fable!
      He's the Lord of creation . . .

Verse 3 may be repeated as a round (from *),
then the chorus sung together.

263
Douglas Coombes
© Lindsay Music †

1 Shepherds, leave your flocks,
      and journey to the manger:
   there in Bethlehem
      you'll find the child, the saviour.
   He is born this night
      to gentle maiden Mary –
   shepherds, come with me,
      this miracle to see.

2 Shepherds, do not fear,
      though winds are getting stronger:
   Bethlehem is near,
      the way is not much longer.
   There's the stable door –
      go in and kneel before him:
   Jesus, gentle king,
      accept the praise we bring!

3 Shepherds, now return,
      with joy your hearts are laden;
   spread the joyful news
      of Jesus and the maiden:
   God has kept his word,
      his Son is born to save us –
   travel on your way,
      sing praise this Christmas Day!

264
© Michael Perry / Jubilate Hymns

1 Shepherds, wake to news of joy –
      God's envoy
      comes to say
   that for you is born a boy
   close in David's town today!

2 Run to greet him – Christ the Lord,
      God's own Word,
      now arrayed
   not with clothes the rich afford,
   but in humble manger laid!

3 Hear the midnight angels' cry,
      through the sky
      ringing still:
   'Glory be to God on high,
   peace on earth – to all, goodwill;
   peace on earth – to all, goodwill!

265
From the Latin
© Michael Perry / Jubilate Hymns

1 Shout aloud, girls and boys!
   Sing today and rejoice,
   lift your heart, raise your voice;
   come and do not waver,
   God has shown us favour:
      virgin-born, born, born,
      virgin-born, born, born,
   virgin-born, Mary's child,
      Christ is here – our saviour!

2 There you lie, Lord of all!
   For your robe – peasant shawl,
   for your bed – ox's stall,
   for your throne a manger,
   homeless as a stranger;
      come to win, win, win,
      come to win, win, win,
   come to win hell's domain –
      spurning death and danger!

3 Even now, from afar
   wise men seek heaven's star,
   bringing gifts where you are:
   gold to bow before you,
   incense to implore you,
      myrrh to say, say, say,
      myrrh to say, say, say,
   myrrh to say 'sacrifice' –
      therefore we adore you!

4 Boys and girls, voices raise!
   Christmas choirs, sweetly phrase
   songs of joy and of praise;
   leave all care and worry,
   sing the angels story:
      Christ is born, born born!
      Christ is born, born born!
   Christ is born: Peace on earth,
      and to God be glory!

266
After J Möhr (1792–1848)
J F Young (1820–1885)

1 Silent night! holy night!
   all is calm, all is bright
   round the virgin and her child:
   holy infant, so gentle and mild,
      sleep in heavenly peace;
      sleep in heavenly peace!

2 Silent night! holy night!
  shepherds quail at the sight,
  glory streams from heaven afar:
  heavenly hosts sing, 'Alleluia,
      Christ the saviour is born,
      Christ the saviour is born.'

3 Silent night! holy night!
  Son of God, love's pure light:
  radiant beams your holy face
  with the dawn of saving grace,
      Jesus, Lord, at your birth,
      Jesus, Lord, at your birth.

267 © Michael Perry / Jubilate Hymns

1 Silver star
      shining out over Bethlehem,
  lead worshippers from afar,
      inspiring and guiding them!
  They look for the infant King –
      with their gifts they will honour him;
  and love in their hearts they bring,
      true service to offer him.

2 Holy night
      for a pilgrim to journey through!
  O traveller, seek the light
      that welcomes and beckons you!
  You come to the brink of heaven,
      to the gateway of paradise;
  for you has the Child been given,
      on you shall the Sun arise.

3 Silent sky
      full of wonder and mystery –
  the splendour of God most high,
      the mantle of majesty!
  Yet God lays aside his crown –
      O give praise to the mighty Lord!
  and for our release comes down –
      O welcome the living Word!

268 Martin Cox
© Ears and Eyes Music †

1 Sing a new song of thanksgiving,
  the Lord is returning to claim his own;
  he's coming back to heal your hurt and pain,
  to harvest all the seed he's sown.
      He's coming back, he's coming back,
      he's coming back to claim his own,
      he's coming back, he's coming back,
      he's coming back,
          and his glory will be shown.

2 Sing a new song to the Saviour,
  stand and name him your Lord and king;
  praise and adore him for he gave his life,
  to conquer fear and death's sharp sting.
      He's coming back . . .

3 Sing a new song to the Bridegroom,
  raise your voices to praise his name;
  be ready to greet him: you'll not know the hour
  when joyfully he'll call your name.
      He's coming back . . .

269 Colleen O'Meara
© Celebration Services / Thankyou Music †

1 Sing a song, a joyful song,
  sing unto the Lord;
  Sing a song, a joyful song,
  sing unto the Lord.
      Clap your hands, all you people,
      clap your hands unto the Lord;
      dance your feet, all you people,
      dance unto the Lord!

2 See the baby in a manger,
  see the baby softly sleeping;
  see the baby in a manger –
  come with me and see.
      Clap your hands . . .

3 See the mother rock the baby,
  rock the baby, rock the baby;
  see the mother rock the baby –
  come with me and see.
      Clap your hands . . .

4 Hear the donkey hee and hawing,
  hee and hawing, hee and hawing;
  hear the donkey hee and hawing,
  come with me and see.
      Clap your hands . . .

5 Shepherds on the hills a-watching,
  hills a-watching, hills a-watching;
  shepherds on the hills a-watching:
  come with me and see.
      Clap your hands . . .

6 See the stars so brightly shining,
  brightly shining, brightly shining;
  see the stars so brightly shining,
  come with me and see.
      Clap your hands . . .

7 Kings upon their camels riding,
  camels riding, camels riding;
  kings upon their camels riding,
  bringing gifts to him.
      Clap your hands . . .

270 Verse 1 © Linda Stassen / New Song Ministries †
verses 2–4 anonymous

1 Sing alleluia to the Lord,
  sing alleluia to the Lord,
  sing alleluia, sing alleluia,
  sing alleluia to the Lord!

2 Jesus is risen from the dead,
  Jesus is risen from the dead,
  Jesus is risen, Jesus is risen,
  Jesus is risen from the dead!

3 Jesus is Lord of heaven and earth,
  Jesus is Lord of heaven and earth,
  Jesus is Lord, Jesus is Lord,
  Jesus is Lord of heaven and earth!

4 Jesus is coming for his own,
  Jesus is coming for his own,
  Jesus is coming, Jesus is coming,
  Jesus is coming for his own.

271
From Psalm 98 (*Cantate Domino*)
© Timothy Dudley-Smith †

1 Sing a new song to the Lord,
he to whom wonders belong!
Rejoice in his triumph
and tell of his power –
O sing to the Lord a new song!

2 Now to the ends of the earth
see his salvation is shown;
and still he remembers
his mercy and truth,
unchanging in love to his own.

3 Sing a new song and rejoice,
publish his praises abroad!
Let voices in chorus,
with trumpet and horn,
resound for the joy of the Lord!

4 Join with the hills and the sea
thunders of praise to prolong!
In judgement and justice
he comes to the earth –
O sing to the Lord a new song!

272
Unknown
© in this version Word & Music / Jubilate Hymns

1 Sing glory, glory alleluia –
angel hosts the skies adorn;
sing glory, g ory alleluia –
our redeemer, Christ is born!

2 Sing glory, glory, alleluia –
tell the news of 'Peace on earth!';
sing glory, glory, alleluia –
come and celebrate his birth!

3 Sing glory, glory, alleluia –
to his city make your way;
sing glory, glory, alleluia –
our redeemer lives today!

OR, ON CHRISTMAS DAY:

3 Sing glory, glory, alleluia –
to his city make your way;
sing glory, glory, alleluia –
Jesus Christ is born today!

273
Bob Fraser
© Ears and Eyes Music †

Sing heaven, shout for joy, O earth;
let the mountains burst into song,
for the saviour comes and he will rule in glory –
your redeemer will not be long.
Alleluia, alleluia, alleluia,
come, Lord Jesus;
alleluia, alleluia, alleluia,
come!

274
S Baring-Gould (1834–1924)

1 Sing lullaby!
lullaby baby, now reclining:
sing lullaby!
Hush, do not wake the infant king;
angels are watching, stars are shining
over the place where he is lying:
sing lullaby.

2 Sing lullaby!
lullaby baby, sweetly sleeping:
sing lullaby!
Hush, do not wake the infant king;
soon will come sorrow with the morning,
soon will come bitter grief and weeping:
sing lullaby!

3 Sing lullaby!
lullaby baby, gently dozing:
sing lullaby!
Hush, do not wake the infant king;
soon comes the cross, the nails, the piercing,
then in the grave at last reposing:
sing lullaby!

4 Sing lullaby!
lullaby! Is the baby waking?
sing lullaby!
Hush, do not stir the infant king;
dreaming of Easter, joyful morning,
conquering death, its bondage breaking:
sing lullaby!

275
© Timothy Dudley-Smith †

1 Soft the evening shadows fall,
still journey on;
darkness soon be over all,
still journey on.
Weary now, and travel-worn,
night must come before the morn:
where will Mary's Son be born?
Still journey on.

2 Shepherds hasten from the fold;
this God has done.
Here in human form behold
this God has done.
Christ the Lord of David's line,
born a saviour and a sign,
King immortal, Child divine,
this God has done.

3 Kings who from the east afar
still journey on,
seeking Christ beneath a star,
still journey on.
For his worship incense bring,
gold to crown an infant King,
myrrh to mark his suffering,
still journey on.

4 Lord of all, enthroned above,
    God sent his Son.
God of everlasting love,
    God sent his Son.
He himself a ransom gave,
bowed himself to cross and grave,
came himself to seek and save,
    God sent his Son.

5 So the Christmas story tell;
    still journey on.
At the last shall all be well;
    still journey on.
Love be ours, and joy and praise,
one with Christ to walk his ways,
in his service all our days
    still journey on.

276 © Paul Wigmore / Jubilate Hymns

1 Softly, a shepherd is singing his song
over the Bethlehem hills all night long:
    Night-time is passing –
    wait for the dawning!
    Praise him who brings us
    joy in the morning:
    Alleluia!

2 Heralding angels are singing their song,
wonderful words that to heaven belong:
    Night-time is passing . . .

3 Lovingly, Mary is singing her song,
bearing the child who will bear all our wrong:
    Night-time is passing . . .

4 Worshipping Jesus, we sing a new song –
Bethlehem's baby, our saviour so strong:
    Night-time is passing . . .

277 © Michael Perry / Jubilate Hymns

1 Songs of gladness,
    songs of gladness
        let us sing,
        let us sing!
    Glory to our Saviour,
    glory to our Saviour
        and our king,
        and our king!

2 Joyful tidings,
    joyful tidings
        ring, bells, ring;
        ring, bells, ring!
    Sound aloud his praises,
    sound aloud his praises:
        Ding-dong, ding,
        ding-dong, ding!

278 © Michael Perry / Jubilate Hymns

1 Soldiers marching
        ta-rata-ta-ta
    the streets of Bethlehem,
        ta-rata-ta-ta
    a little king to find
        ta-rata-ta-ta
    for Herod's peace of mind,
        ta-rata-ta-ta
        rata-ta-ta, rata-ta-ta
    since the wise men spoke
        ta-rata-ta-ta
    of a star.

2 Soldiers knocking
        ta-rata-ta-ta
    on doors of Bethlehem,
        ta-rata-ta-ta
    obeying Herod's will
        ta-rata-ta-ta
    all infant boys to kill,
        ta-rata-ta-ta
        rata-ta-ta, rata-ta-ta
    paying well to know
        ta-rata-ta-ta
    where they are.

3 Soldiers marching
        ta-rata-ta-ta
    away from Bethlehem,
        ta-rata-ta-ta
    despising mothers' cries,
        ta-rata-ta-ta
    to Herod telling lies:
        ta-rata-ta-ta
        rata-ta-ta, rata-ta-ta
    Jesus whom they seek
        ta-rata-ta-ta
    is afar.

279 Andrae Crouch © Lexicon Music Incorporated / Crouch Music (USA) / Word Music (UK) †

1 Soon – and very soon –
    we are going to see the King *
        Alleluia, alleluia,
        we're going to see the King!

2 No more crying there . . . *
        Alleluia . . .

3 No more dying there . . . *
        Alleluia . . .

    Alleluia, alleluia, alleluia, alleluia!

4 Soon and very soon . . . *
        Alleluia . . .

    Alleluia, alleluia, alleluia, alleluia!

* These sentences are twice repeated.

280

Sound on the trumpet,
call to the people,
sing your new song –
our Bridegroom's coming,
it won't be long.

Break out the banners,
join in the dancing,
no time for gloom –
prepare the banquet,
he's coming soon.

1 If you're one of God's people,
rejoice in praise and song;
come lift up your hearts before him
and give your voices in praise and song.
Sound on the trumpet . . .

2 Go out in tears and weeping
to bring the harvest home:
it's time for the joy of reaping;
in joy the sheaves now are coming home.
Sound on the trumpet . . .

Yes!

281

1 Still, still, still,
the baby lies asleep:
yet far away are herald voices –
heaven sings and earth rejoices!
Still, still, still,
the baby lies asleep.

2 Love, love, love,
no greater love than his;
while 'Christ the Lord' the angels name him,
we with fervent hearts acclaim him.
Love, love, love,
no greater love than his!

282

Standing in the rain,
knocking on the window,
knocking on the window
on a Christmas day.

There he is again,
knocking on the window,
knocking on the window
in the same old way.

1 No use knocking on the window,
there is nothing we can do, sir;
all the beds are booked already,
there is nothing left for you, sir!
Standing in the rain . . .

2 No, we haven't got a manger,
no, we haven't got a stable:
till you woke us with your knocking,
we were sleeping like the dead, sir!
Standing in the rain . . .

283

1 Sweet was the song that Mary sang
when she to Bethlehem Judah came,
and was delivered of a son –
the saviour, Jesus Christ by name:
'Lullaby, lullaby;
lullaby, lullaby.'

2 'Sweet babe,' she sang, 'my darling son,
for our salvation timely born,
whom God has promised from on high
to visit those by sorrow worn!'
'Lullaby, sweet babe,' she sang,
and rocked him gently on her knee.

284

1 Take heart and praise our God;
rejoice and clap your hands –
his power our foe subdued,
his mercy ever stands:
let trumpets sound and people sing,
the Lord through all the earth is king!

2 Take heart, but sing with fear,
exalt his worthy name;
with mind alert and clear
now celebrate his fame:
let trumpets sound . . .

3 Take heart for future days,
for tasks as yet unknown –
the God whose name we praise
is seated on the throne:
let trumpets sound . . .

4 Take heart and trust in God
the Father and the Son –
God is our strength and shield,
his Spirit guides us on:
let trumpets sound . . .

285

1 Tell out, my soul, the greatness of the Lord!
unnumbered blessings give my spirit voice;
tender to me the promise of his word;
in God my saviour shall my heart rejoice.

2 Tell out, my soul, the greatness of his name!
make known his might,
the deeds his arm has done;
his mercy sure, from age to age the same;
his holy name – the Lord, the mighty one.

3 Tell out, my soul, the greatness of his might!
powers and dominions lay their glory by.
Proud hearts and stubborn wills are put to flight,
the hungry fed, the humble lifted high.

4 Tell out, my soul, the glories of his word!
firm is his promise, and his mercy sure.
Tell out, my soul, the greatness of the Lord
to children's children and for evermore!

286
S Baring Gould (1834–1924)
© in this version Word & Music / Jubilate Hymns

1 The angel Gabriel from heaven came,
his wings as drifted snow, his eyes as flame:
'From God, all hail,' the angel said to Mary,
    'most highly favoured lady!'
    Gloria!

2 'Fear not, for you shall bear a holy child,
by him shall we to God be reconciled;
his name shall be Emmanuel, the long-foretold:
    most highly favoured lady!'
    Gloria!

3 Then gentle Mary humbly bowed her head:
'To me be as it pleases God,' she said,
'My soul shall praise and magnify
        his holy name.'
    Most highly favoured lady!
    Gloria!

4 'And so,' she said, 'how happy I shall be!
All generations will remember me;
for God has kept his promises to Israel.'
    Most highly favoured lady!
    Gloria!

5 Of her, Emmanuel – the Christ – was born
in Bethlehem, upon that Christmas morn.
And Christian folk throughout the world
        will ever say,
    'Most highly favoured lady!
    Gloria!'

287
From Matthew 25
Graham Kendrick
© Thankyou Music †

    Tell me, why do you weep;
    tell me, why do you mourn;
    tell me, why do you look so sad?
    Tell me, why don't you dance;
    tell me, why don't you sing;
    tell me, why don't you look to the sky?

1 Don't you know that your king is coming;
don't you know that your king is nigh?
He is even at the gates of Jerusalem,
he is coming on the morning sky.
    Tell me . . .

2 Don't you know that the feast is ready –
ready for the bride to come?
Christians, keep your lamps a-burning –
the ending of the age is come.
    Tell me . . .

3 Don't you know you are the Lord's invited;
don't you know you are the chosen ones?
You in whom he has delighted
shall rise with Jesus when he comes.
    Tell me . . .

4 Come arise, my love, my fairest daughter:
the winter and the rain are gone,
the flowers of summer are appearing,
the time of singing songs has come.
    Tell me . . .

5 Don't you know that your king is coming;
Don't you know that your king is nigh?
He is even at the gates of Jerusalem,
he is coming on the morning sky.

288
Miriam Richards
© Salvationist Publishing and Supplies †
and in this version Word & Music / Jubilate Hymns

1 The bells ring out at Christmas-time
their message loud and clear;
our hearts are stirred as on the air
the joyful sound we hear:
    Ring out the Christmas bells,
    ring out the Christmas bells!
        The saviour comes –
        make straight his way,
    ring out those bells!
        The saviour comes –
        make straight his way,
    ring out those bells!

2 Thanks be to God, since all may learn
the bells' exultant theme –
the babe of Bethlehem was born
this lost world to redeem:
    Ring out . . .

3 Glad message of the Christmas bells,
of God whose name is love –
O may this music all our days
our hope and comfort prove!
    Ring out . . .

289/290
© Timothy Dudley-Smith †

1 The darkness turns to dawn,
the dayspring shines from heaven;
for unto us a child is born,
to us a Son is given.

2 The Son of God most high,
before all else began,
a virgin's son behold him lie,
the new-born Son of Man.

3 God's Word of truth and grace
made flesh with us to dwell;
the brightness of the Father's face,
the child Emmanuel.

4 How rich his heavenly home!
How poor his human birth!
As mortal man he stoops to come,
the light and life of earth.

5 A servant's form, a slave,
the Lord consents to share;
our sin and shame, our cross and grave,
he bows himself to bear.

6 Obedient and alone
upon that cross to die,
and then to share the Father's throne
in majesty on high.

7 And still God sheds abroad
that love so strong to send
a saviour, who is Christ the Lord,
whose reign shall never end.

291
John Daniels and Phil Thomson
© Ears and Eyes Music †

1 The earth was dark until you spoke –
then all was light and all was peace;
yet still, O God, so many wait
to see the flame of love released.
Lights to the world!
O Light divine,
kindle in us a mighty flame,
till every heart, consumed by love
shall rise to praise your holy name!

2 In Christ you gave your gift of life
to save us from the depths of night:
O come and set our spirits free
and draw us to your perfect light!
Lights to the world . . .

3 Where there is fear may we bring joy,
and healing to a world of pain:
Lord, build your kingdom through our lives
till Jesus walks this earth again.
Lights to the world . . .

4 O burn in us, that we may burn
with love that triumphs in despair;
and touch our lives with such a fire
that souls may search and find you there.
Lights to the world . . .

292
Unknown (c. seventeenth century)
© in this version Word & Music / Jubilate Hymns

1 The first nowell the angel did say,
was to Bethlehem's shepherds
in fields as they lay;
in fields where they lay keeping their sheep
on a cold winter's night that was so deep:
Nowell, nowell, nowell, nowell,
born is the king of Israel!

2 Then wise men from a country far
looked up and saw a guiding star;
they travelled on by night and day
to reach the place where Jesus lay:
Nowell, nowell . . .

3 At Bethlehem they entered in,
on bended knee they worshipped him;
they offered there in his presence
their gold and myrrh and frankincense:
Nowell, nowell . . .

4 Then let us all with one accord
sing praises to our heavenly Lord;
for Christ has our salvation wrought
and with his blood our life has bought:
Nowell, nowell . . .

293
B Rees (1911–1983)
© Mrs M Rees

1 The God we seek, beyond all thought,
has now his Christmas wonder wrought:
behold, the seeker is the sought!
Waiting ended,
earth befriended –
Jesus is born!

2 Love is the manger where he lies,
love is the cross on which he dies:
stronger than death shall love arise!
Glorious meekness,
power in weakness –
Jesus is born!

3 Into the love of Christ the king
our lives, our world, in faith we bring:
the sin, the pain, the suffering.
God esteems us,
Christ redeems us –
Jesus is born!

294
Don Wyrtzen
© Singspiration Music /
Universal Songs BV / Cherry Pie Music †

1 The heaviness of travel
to an over-crowded town
had pressed down on the simple girl,
who rode without a sound;
already now the quiet pain
of childbirth had begun,
and all the inns turned them away –
was there no room for God's only Son?

2 No royal home was open
to the weary man and his wife,
but only a stable cave was left
to greet the cry of life;
the sheep and oxen shared the joy
that made all heaven sing:
that straw-strewn cave was changed
into the birthplace of the King.

295
Traditional
© in this version Word & Music / Jubilate Hymns

1 The holly and the ivy
when they are both full grown –
of all the trees that are in the wood,
the holly bears the crown.
Oh, the rising of the sun
and the running of the deer,
the playing of the merry organ,
sweet singing in the choir!

2 The holly bears a blossom
as white as any flower;
and Mary bore sweet Jesus Christ
to be our sweet saviour.
Oh, the rising . . .

3 The holly bears a berry
as red as any blood;
and Mary bore sweet Jesus Christ
to die for all our good.
Oh, the rising . . .

4 The holly bears a prickle,
   as sharp as any thorn;
and Mary bore sweet Jesus Christ
to wear a cruel crown.
   Oh, the rising . . .

5 The holly bears a bark
   as bitter as any gall;
and Mary bore sweet Jesus Christ
to suffer for us all.
   Oh, the rising . . .

6 The holly and the ivy
   when they are both full grown –
of all the trees that are in the wood,
the holly bears the crown.
   Oh, the rising . . .

296

From John 3 etc
Don Fishel
© Word of God Music †

   The light of Christ has come
   into the world,
   the light of Christ
   has come into the world.

1 We all must be born again
     to see the kingdom of God;
the water and the Spirit bring
     new life in God's love.
   The light of Christ . . .

2 God gave up his only Son
     out of love for the world,
so that all those who believe in him
will live for ever.
   The light of Christ . . .

3 The light of God has come to us
     so that we might have salvation;
from the darkness of our sins we walk
     into glory with Christ Jesus.
   The light of Christ . . .

297

Alice Pullen (1889–1983)
© Miss D M Gill
and in this version Word & Music / Jubilate Hymns

1 The little baby Jesus is asleep –
   if you tiptoe very softly you may peep:
can you see him in the hay
on this happy Christmas day?
   Hush! he's asleep.

2 The little baby Jesus is asleep,
   the shepherds in the fields have left their sheep;
they have heard the angels sing,
and have come to find their king.
   Hush! he's asleep.

3 The little baby Jesus is asleep –
   he is far too small to walk, or even creep;
but the story's just begun
for he is God's only Son.
   Hush! he's asleep.

298

From Isaiah 9
J Morison (1750–1798)
© in this version Jubilate Hymns

1 The people who in darkness walked
   have seen a glorious light:
that light shines out on those who lived
in shadows of the night.

2 To greet you, Sun of righteousness,
   the gathering nations come;
rejoicing as when reapers bring
their harvest treasures home.

3 For now to us a child is born,
   to us a son is given;
and on his shoulder ever rests
all power in earth and heaven.

4 His name shall be the prince of peace,
   eternally adored;
most wonderful of counsellors,
the great and mighty Lord.

5 His peace and righteous government
   shall over all extend;
on judgement and on justice based,
his reign shall never end.

299

Graham Kendrick
© Thankyou Music †

1 The Lord is king,
     he is mighty in battle,
working wonders,
     glorious in majesty.

2 The Lord is king –
     so majestic in power!
His right hand
     has shattered the enemy.

3 ᴬThis is my God
     and I will praise him;
ᴮthis is my God
     and I will praise him:

4 ᴬMy strength and song
   · and my salvation,
ᴮmy strength and song
   ᴬᴸᴸand my salvation.

(* The singers may divide at A and B)

300

© Michael Perry / Jubilate Hymns

1 The shepherd guards his sheep
   upon the hillside late at night –
he is woken from his sleep
to see a flash of blinding light,
a voice that makes him leap
proclaims the news with great delight
that Jesus Christ is born!
   Glory, glory, alleluia;
   glory, glory, alleluia;
   glory, glory, alleluia –
   for Jesus Christ is born!

2 The wise man in the east
  is glad to see the shining star –
  he is saddling up his beast
  to go to Bethlehem afar:
  we find our king and priest,
  salvation comes where sinners are
  as Jesus Christ is born!
    Glory, glory, alleluia;
    glory, glory, alleluia;
    glory, glory, alleluia –
    for Jesus Christ is born!

3 So let us make our pleasure
  humble service to the king
  as we offer him our treasure
  and the praises that we bring:
  with love in fullest measure
  God has blessed us – so we sing
  that Jesus Christ is born!
    Glory, glory . . .

301 Dottie Rambo
© John T Benson Publishing Company /
Universal Songs BV / Cherry Pie Music †

1 The sky shall unfold preparing his entrance,
  the stars will applaud him
        with thunders of praise;
  the sweet light in his eyes
        shall enhance those awaiting,
    we shall behold him – then, face to face.
  We shall behold him, we shall behold him –
  face to face in all of his glory;
  we shall behold him, we shall behold him,
  face to face, our saviour and Lord!

2 The angel shall sound the shout of his coming,
  the sleeping will rise
        from their slumbering place;
  and those who remain
        shall be changed in a moment,
    and we shall behold him – then,
        face to face.
  We shall behold . . .

  Face to face, our saviour and Lord;
  face to face, our saviour and Lord!

302 From Matthew 2
David Jenkins
© 1969 Boosey & Hawkes Music Publishers Ltd †

1 The star in the east
        shone bright over Bethlehem,
  clear in the evening sky;
  that was the night when they heard
        in Bethlehem
  the sound of a baby's cry:
  for there was born in a humble manger
  an unknown child, just a little stranger.
    But three wise men who came and adored,
    knew he was Christ, our Lord.

2 The star in the east, so bright over Bethlehem,
  shines in the world today;
  Jesus Christ, who was born in Bethlehem
  shows us the righteous way:
  leaders may rise with their new philosophies,
  but deep in our hearts
  are the ancient prophesies
        that God's own Son the wise men adored
        is destined to be our Lord.

3 The time will come when the star of Bethlehem
  gleams once again in the sky;
  and on that night the star of Bethlehem
  will shine like a flame on high:
  and who will return to a new creation,
  and bring to a suffering world salvation?
        The king the three wise men adored –
        Jesus Christ our Lord.

303 Barbara Gillard
© St Paul's Outreach Trust †

1 The stars danced, the angels sang
  the night God came to earth;
  the whole vault of heaven rang
  to celebrate his birth.
        We will dance, we will sing,
        we will praise our heavenly king
        at his birth.

2 Mary, his mother, smiled
  to see her babe new-born.
  Shepherds came hurrying,
  left their flocks forlorn.
        We will dance . . .

3 Wise men who saw his star,
  knew their Lord was here,
  came with their offerings,
  incense, gold and myrrh.
        We will dance . . .

4 We too will give to him,
  gifts of love and praise,
  dance for him, sing for him,
  rejoice in him always.
        We will dance . . .

304 © Michael Perry / Jubilate Hymns

1 The story has broken,
  an angel has spoken,
  and this is the token
        that Jesus is here:
  he comes as a stranger
  regardless of danger,
  the Lord in a manger,
        the babe without peer.

2 O counsel of splendour,
  O sacrifice tender,
  that God should surrender
        to us in this way –
  his purpose revealing,
  his promises sealing,
  the pledge of our healing,
        the dawn of our day!

3 The shepherds returning,
 and wise men of learning
 their saviour discerning,
  his praises will sing:
 as those who first saw him
 and knelt down before him,
 so let us adore him
  and worship our king.

4 O infinite treasure,
 O love without measure,
 it is God's good pleasure
  to give us his Son,
 the source of creation,
 the hope of each nation,
 the great jubilation
  of heaven begun!

305
West Indian carol
© 1945 collected Boosey & Co Ltd †

1 The virgin Mary had a baby boy,
 the virgin Mary had a baby boy,
 the virgin Mary had a baby boy
 and they say that his name is Jesus.
  He come from the glory,
  he come from the glorious kingdom;
  (Yes!) he come from the glory,
  he come from the glorious kingdom:
   O yes, believer!
   O yes, believer!
  He come from the glory,
  he come from the glorious kingdom.
   O yes ...

2 The angels sang when the baby was born,
 the angels sang when the baby was born,
 the angels sang when the baby was born
 and they sang that his name is Jesus.
  He come from the glory ...

3 The shepherds came where the baby was born,
 the shepherds came where the baby was born,
 the shepherds came where the baby was born
 and they say that his name is Jesus.
  He come from the glory ...

306
Unknown
© in this version Word & Music / Jubilate Hymns

1 The wise may bring their learning,
  the rich may bring their wealth,
 and some may bring their greatness,
  and some their strength and health;
 we too would bring our treasures
  to offer to the king:
 how shall we greet our saviour,
  what presents shall we bring?

2 We'll bring the many duties
  we have to do each day,
 we'll try our best to please him,
  at home, at work, at play;
 and better are these treasures
  to offer to the king,
 than richest gifts without them –
  yet these we all may bring.

3 We'll bring him hearts that love him,
  we'll bring him thankful praise,
 and lives for ever striving
  to follow in his ways;
 and these shall be the treasures
  we offer to the king,
 the gifts that now and ever
  our grateful hearts may bring!

307
Melody Green
© Birdwing Music / Cherry Lane Music Limited †

1 There is a Redeemer,
 Jesus, God's own Son,
 precious Lamb of God, Messiah,
 holy One.
  Thank you, O my Father,
  for giving us your Son,
  and leaving your Spirit
  till the work on earth is done.

2 Jesus, my Redeemer,
 name above all names,
 precious Son of God, Messiah,
 Lamb for sinners slain:
  Thank you ...

3 When I stand in glory,
 I will see his face
 and there I'll serve my king for ever
 in that holy place.
  Thank you ...

308
© Michael Perry / Jubilate Hymns

1 There's a bright sky over Bethlehem,
 where shepherds watch upon the hill:
  and the heavens ring
  as angels sing
 of peace on earth and God's goodwill!

2 There's a saviour come to Bethlehem,
 a baby laid upon the hay:
  in a stable bare
  no comfort where
 the Christ is born this holy day.

3 There's a star high over Bethlehem –
 the wise men start upon the road:
  bearing gold and myrrh
  and incense rare
 they come to find the Son of God.

4 There's a sign for us in Bethlehem,
 for we rejoice at Christmastide
  to receive our Lord,
  God's living Word,
 our love, our light, our friend, our guide!

309
Traditional
© in this version Word & Music / Jubilate Hymns

1 There's a Saviour to see on Christmas morn –
 rise up, shepherd, and follow;
 we will show you the place
  where the Child is born –
 rise up shepherd and follow!

Leave your sheep
and leave your lambs –
rise up, shepherd, and follow;
leave your sheep
and leave your rams –
rise up, shepherd, and follow!

Follow, follow,
rise up, shepherd, and follow,
hark to the angels of Bethlehem –
rise up, shepherd, and follow!

2 If you take good heed to the angel's words –
rise up, shepherd, and follow,
you'll forget your flocks,
you'll forget your herds –
rise up, shepherd, and follow!
Leave your sheep . . .

311 © Anthony Greening

*Sing in praise of God today:
our saviour Christ is born!

1 Today the Christ is born,
today our saviour comes;
today the angels sing,
archangels chant their joy.
*Sing in praise . . .

2 Today the just rejoice,
today they join in song –
'To God on high be praise,
on earth as now in heaven!'
*Sing in praise . . .

3 Today sing praise to God –
the Father and the Son,
who with the Spirit reign
for ever Three in One:
*Sing in praise . . .

*Original text: Jubilate Deo:/Salvator natus est.

310 From Genesis 3 etc
© Chris Voke

1 These were the words – God to Adam:
you are a rebel banished from light;
from the serpent and his evil
you will find death and sorrow and night.
This was the promise to all people:
from the woman a saviour will come;
by his living and his dying
he will bring life again.

2 These were the words – God to Abraham:
look to the heavens, number the stars –
your descendants shall be as many;
but One shall shine much brighter than all.
This is the promise for all people:
he will be born of Abraham's line,
he will bring back the blessing of heaven
to every family on earth.

3 These were the words – God to the prophet:
wait for the baby, look for my Son –
Wonderful Counsellor, God so Mighty,
Eternal Father, yet Prince of peace.
This was the promise to all people:
he will be ruler of heaven and earth;
his great kingdom and his power
shall never be taken away.

4 These were the words – God to the shepherds:
go to the village, look for the child –
he is the saviour born among you,
God in a stable, far from the light.
This is the promise to all people:
those who receive him as Jesus the Lord,
he gives mercy, life, and power
to be a child of God.

(...the little Lord Jesus asleep on the hay.)

312 From Psalm 24
© Christopher Idle / Jubilate Hymns

1 This earth belongs to God,
the world, its wealth, and all its people;
he formed the waters wide
and fashioned every sea and shore.
AWho may go up the hill of the Lord
and stand in the place of holiness?
BOnly the one whose heart is pure,
whose hands and lips are clean.

2 Lift high your heads, you gates,
rise up, you everlasting doors, as
here now the king of glory
enters into full command.
AWho is the king, this king of glory,
where is the throne he comes to claim?
BChrist is the king, the Lord of glory,
fresh from his victory.

3 Lift high your heads, you gates,
and fling wide open the ancient doors, for
here comes the king of glory
taking universal power.
AWho is the king, this king of glory,
what is the power by which he reigns?
BChrist is the king, his cross his glory,
and by love he rules.

4 All glory be to God
the Father, Son, and Holy Spirit;
from ages past it was,
is now, and evermore shall be.

(* The congregation may divide at A and B)

313

Elaine Davies
© Mustard Seed Music †

This night a miracle happened –
a boy child was born.
Go spread the news: from today
a new era will dawn.

1 Glorious things tonight are happening –
who can disbelieve their sight?
royal kings will pay him homage,
yes, coming to find this town tonight!
For, this night . . .

2 Angels sing their heavenly choruses
to the babe, the King of kings –
he who is the truth and glory,
a light to the darkness he will bring.
For, this night . . .

314

From Christmas Jazz
Kenneth Cartwright
© 1969 Boosey & Hawkes Music Publishers Ltd †

1 Though Mary of Nazareth, that maiden so mild,
was told by an angel that she was with child,
to Bethlehem city to go she was told
to journey with Joseph
        through nights bleak and cold.

2 They borrowed a donkey to help get them there,
their clothing and bedding and luggage to bear.
They travelled on foot on a rough dusty road,
for three days and nights
        they toiled with their load.

3 On a clear frosty night to this place in Judea
Mary and Joseph and donkey drew near.
But when they arrived at the inn they did find
no comfort or shield from the cold winter wind.

4 At last in a stable they find room to rest.
A place for a baby? It's hardly the best!
But there in that stable
        that first Christmas morn,
while people were sleeping, Jesus was born.

315

From Psalm 108
Dale Garratt
© Scripture in Song / Thankyou Music †

Through our God we shall do valiantly –
it is he who will tread down our enemies;
we'll sing and shout his victory:
Christ is king!

For God has won the victory
and set his people free,
his word has slain the enemy,
the earth shall stand and see
that
        Through our God . . .

Christ is king,
Christ is king,
Christ is king!

316

After F Fletcher (1870–1954)
© Oxford University Press †
and in this version Word & Music / Jubilate Hymns

1 To people of goodwill,
be peace on earth and gladness!
Let joyful carols fill
the world where once was sadness.
    So let us on this morn
    lift up our hearts to heaven:
    to us a Child is born,
    to us a Son is given:
    O praise him, O praise him, O praise him!

2 Through pain of sin's distress,
all worldly pride unheeding,
in paths of righteousness
a little child is leading:
    So let us . . .

3 All you that burdens bear,
come, take his yoke upon you:
your work he comes to share,
and lays his light load on you:
    So let us . . .

4 O holy, humble birth –
now sing the joyful story!
Good will, good will on earth,
and in the highest glory!
    So let us . . .

317

C Wesley (1707–1788)
© in this version Word & Music / Jubilate Hymns

1 To us a child of royal birth,
the heir of promises is given;
invisible, yet here on earth,
the Son of Man, the God of heaven.

2 A saviour born, in love supreme
he comes our fallen souls to raise;
he comes his people to redeem
with all the fulness of his grace.

3 The Christ foretold by prophecy
and filled with all the Spirit's power,
our prophet, priest and king is he,
the mighty Lord whom we adore.

4 The Lord of hosts, the God most high
who leaves his throne to live on earth,
with joy we welcome from the sky
and take into our hearts by faith.

318 Graham Kendrick

MEN'S VOICES
We declare that the kingdom of God is here,
TREBLE VOICES
we declare that the kingdom of God is here,
MEN'S VOICES
we declare that the kingdom of God is here,
TREBLE VOICES
we declare that the kingdom of God is here
MEN'S VOICES
among you,
TREBLE VOICES
among you,
MEN'S VOICES
among you,
TREBLE VOICES
among you.

MEN'S VOICES
We declare . . .

ALL
The blind see, the deaf hear,
the lame men are walking,
sicknesses flee at his voice;
the dead live again
and the poor hear the good news:
Jesus is king – so rejoice!

MEN'S VOICES
We declare that the kingdom of God is here,
TREBLE VOICES
we declare that the kingdom of God is here,
MEN'S VOICES
we declare that the
ALL
kingdom of God is here!

319 Traditional

We believe this is Jesus –
come and see, come and see;
we believe this is Jesus –
come and see, come and see.

1 The light of God lights up his face –
come and see, come and see;
he offers us redeeming grace –
come and see, come and see.
We believe . . .

2 The love of God shines in his eyes –
come and see, come and see;
it tells of glory in the skies –
come and see, come and see.
We believe . . .

3 Did you ever see such love before –
come and see, come and see?
Go in peace and sin no more –
come and see, come and see!
We believe . . .

320 Mosie Lister

1 We have reason to rejoice,
to rejoice, to rejoice:
we have reason to rejoice:
Christ the Lord is born.
We have reason now to sing,
now to sing, now to sing;
we have reason now to sing:
Christ the Lord is born.
Sing Alleluia!
Christ is born, Christ is born.
Alleluia –
Christ is born in Bethlehem!

2 Tell the nations everywhere,
everywhere, everywhere;
tell the nations everywhere:
Christ the Lord is born.
Lift your voice and sing it out,
sing it out, sing it out.
Lift your voice and sing it out:
Christ the Lord is born.
Sing Alleluia . . .

321 J H Hopkins (1820–1891)

1 ALL
We three kings of orient are,
bearing gifts we travel afar –
field and fountain, moor and mountain –
following yonder star.
O star of wonder, star of night,
star with royal beauty bright:
westward leading, still proceeding,
guide us to your perfect light!

2 FIRST
Born a king on Bethlehem's plain –
gold I bring to crown him again:
king for ever, ceasing never,
over us all to reign.
ALL O star of wonder . . .

3 SECOND
Frankincense to offer have I –
incense tells of Deity nigh;
prayer and praising all are raising:
worship him – God most high!
ALL O star of wonder . . .

4 THIRD
Myrrh is mine – its bitter perfume
breathes a life of gathering gloom:
sorrowing, sighing, bleeding, dying,
sealed in the stone-cold tomb.
ALL O star of wonder . . .

5 ALL
Glorious now behold him arise –
king and God and sacrifice!
Heaven sings 'Alleluia!' –
'Alleluia!' the earth replies.
O star of wonder . . .

322
© Paul Wigmore / Jubilate Hymns

1 We were not there in Bethlehem
with shepherds in the night;
we could not see in starry sky
the dawn of heaven's light –
and yet it shone for us.

2 We were not there in Bethlehem
where Mary laid her son;
we could not see in manger bed
his life on earth begun –
and yet he lived for us.

323
D Trotter
© Copyright controlled †

1 We worship and adore you,
we bow down before you;
you are the Lord, the King of kings,
you are exalted over all things.
  Alleluia, alleluia, alleluia;
  alleluia, alleluia, alleluia!

2 We lift our hands, we lift our hearts,
we lift our voices up to you, O Lord:
all glory and honour and praise,
be yours for evermore!
  Alleluia . . .

324
© in this version Word & Music / Jubilate Hymns

1 We wish you a merry Christmas,
we wish you a merry Christmas,
we wish you a merry Christmas,
and a happy new year!
  Good tidings we bring
  of Jesus your king;
  we wish you a merry Christmas
  and a happy new year!

2 We'll sing you a Christmas carol,
we'll sing you a Christmas carol,
we'll sing you a Christmas carol,
so quickly draw near!
  Good tidings . . .

3 We'll tell you the Christmas story,
we'll tell you the Christmas story,
we'll tell you the Christmas story,
so make sure you hear!
  Good tidings . . .

4 We wish you a merry Christmas,
we wish you a merry Christmas,
we wish you a merry Christmas,
and a happy new year!
  Good tidings . . .

325
Diane Fung
© Springtide / Word Music (UK) †

We'll sing a new song of glorious triumph,
for we see the government of God
  in our lives.
We'll sing . . .

He is crowned – God of the whole world,
crowned king of creation,
crowned – ruling the nations now.
Yes, he is crowned . . .

326
From the Dutch
© Michael Perry / Jubilate Hymns

1 Welcome, Child of Mary,
  coming from above –
our visitor from heaven,
  our Lord of love!
Jesus, dearest saviour,
all praise is yours by right,
now returned to glory,
beyond our human sight.
  Have mercy, Lord!

2 Shepherds in the pasture
  hearing angels sing,
receive with joy and wonder
  the news they bring:
'Go to seek your saviour;
now swiftly make your way –
you will surely find him
in Bethlehem today!'
  Have mercy, Lord!

3 Wise men from the orient,
  skilled to understand
the star that lights the heavens
  their eyes have scanned:
soon they find the saviour
and bring him presents rare,
who can keep our treasure
secure within his care.
  Have mercy, Lord!

327
F Roy Bennett
© Edwin Ashdown Ltd /
William Elkin Music Services †

1 Welcome the Christ-child, Jesus our Saviour,
  born for us all this day:
meekly he lies there, peacefully sleeping,
  cradled amid the hay.
Come now before him, kneel and adore him,
  honour the King of kings;
welcome the Christ-child, born in the manger –
  gladness and joy he brings!

2 Shepherds on hillsides hear of his coming,
  swiftly they leave their fold;
wise men come riding, rare gifts to bring him –
  frankincense, myrrh and gold.
Heaven is ringing, angels are singing,
  telling of Jesus' birth:
welcome the Christ-child, born in the manger,
  king of all heaven and earth.

328

1 Welcome, Jesus child of Mary,
David's son and Judah's star!
  Alleluia, alleluia,
  alleluia, gloria!

2 Welcome, Jesus child of Mary,
come to us from realms afar –
  Alleluia . . .

329

1 Welcome your king – Alleluia!
lands of the sunrise;
travellers, sing, 'Alleluia!',
lift up your tired eyes:
  Come and praise him,
  joyful raise him
  lowly carols of love;
  bow before him
  and adore him –
  Lord from above.

2 Follow his star – Alleluia!
Christ who enthralls you;
seek him from far. Alleluia,
Bethlehem calls you!
  Come and praise him . . .

3 Incense and gold – Alleluia!
these you may borrow;
priest-king foretold – Alleluia!
myrrh for his sorrow.
  Come and praise him . . .

330

1 Welcome, welcome,
saviour born in Bethlehem;
'Glory, glory',
heaven's angels say:
Welcome, welcome –
we shall join to sing with them,
'Glory, glory:
Christ is Lord today!'

2 Welcome, welcome,
God in our humanity;
Glory glory,
praise him and adore:
welcome, welcome,
spurning princely vanity,
Glory, glory,
God among the poor.

3 Welcome, welcome –
lift your voices everyone;
Glory, glory,
sing with glad acclaim:
Welcome, welcome,
welcome God's belovèd Son:
Glory, glory,
glory to his name!

331

1 What can I give to the King,
give to the one, who has everything;
what can I give, what gift can I bring?
What can I give to the King;
what can I give to the King?

2 Give him a heart that's opened up wide,
give him a life that's got nothing to hide,
give him a love that's tender and true,
and he'll give it all back to you;
yes, he'll give it all back to you.

3 What can we give to the King,
give to the one who has everything;
what can we give, what gift can we bring?
What can we give to the King;
what can we give to the King?

4 Give him all glory, his people on earth;
give him all praises this time of his birth;
give him all honour in all that we do:
as he's given his life to you,
as he's given his life to you.

5 What can we give to the King,
give to the one who has everything?
What can we give to the King;
what can we give to the King?

332

1 ALL
When God from heaven to earth came down
  on Christmas Day, on Christmas Day,
the songs rang out in Bethlehem town
  on Christmas Day in the morning.

2 WOMEN AND GIRLS
For Christ was born to save us all,
  on Christmas Day, on Christmas Day,
and laid within a manger stall
  on Christmas Day in the morning.

3 MEN AND BOYS
The shepherds heard the angels sing
  on Christmas Day, on Christmas Day,
to tell them of the saviour-king
  on Christmas Day in the morning.

4 ALL
Now joy is ours and all is well,
  on Christmas Day, on Christmas Day,
so sound the organ, chime the bell
  on Christmas Day in the morning.

333

1 When shepherds watched and angels sang
and Judah's hills with glory rang,
then Christ was born the Son of Man
on Christmas Day in the morning:
  Christ was born the Son of Man
  on Christmas Day, on Christmas Day;
  Christ was born the Son of Man
  on Christmas Day in the morning.

2 Where Joseph knelt and Mary bowed
   and beasts of burden brayed aloud,
   there Christ was born for all our good
   on Christmas Day in the morning:
      Christ was born for all our good
      on Christmas Day, on Christmas Day;
      Christ was born for all our good
      on Christmas Day in the morning.

3 When wise men sought and Herod feared
   and when a royal star appeared,
   then Christ was born to be our Lord
   on Christmas Day in the morning:
      Christ was born to be our Lord
      on Christmas Day, on Christmas Day;
      Christ was born to be our Lord
      on Christmas Day in the morning.

4 Where God no longer calls in vain
   and human hearts are love's domain,
   there Christ is born in us again
   on Christmas Day in the morning:
      Christ is born in us again
      on Christmas Day, on Christmas Day;
      Christ is born in us again
      on Christmas Day in the morning.

334
After the traditional carol
© Michael Perry / Jubilate Hymns

1 When the angel came to Mary,
   he said, 'Be at peace,
   for the Lord God shall be with you,
   his love will not cease.'
      And Mary bore Jesus Christ,
      our saviour for to be;
      and the first and the last
      and the greatest is he,
      is he, is he;
      and the first and the last
      and the greatest is he.

2 When the angel came to Mary,
   he said, 'Do not fear,
   for his power shall be upon you,
   a child you will bear.'
      And Mary bore . . .

3 When the angel came to Mary,
   he said, 'Hear his name,
   for his title shall be Jesus
   of kingly acclaim.'
      And Mary bore . . .

4 When the angel came to Mary,
   she said, 'Be it so:
   for the Lord God is my master,
   his will I must do.'
      And Mary bore . . .

335
From Isaiah 35
© Christopher Idle / Jubilate Hymns

1 When the King shall come again
      all his power revealing,
   splendour shall announce his reign,
      life and joy and healing:
   earth no longer in decay,
      hope no more frustrated;
   this is God's redemption day
      longingly awaited.

2 In the desert trees take root
      fresh from his creation;
   plants and flowers and sweetest fruit
      join the celebration:
   rivers spring up from the earth,
      barren lands adorning;
   valleys, this is your new birth,
      mountains, greet the morning!

3 Strengthen feeble hands and knees,
      fainting hearts, be cheerful!
   God who comes for such as these
      seeks and saves the fearful:
   now the deaf can hear the dumb
      sing away their weeping;
   blind eyes see the injured come
      walking, running, leaping.

4 There God's highway shall be seen
      where no roaring lion,
   nothing evil or unclean
      walks the road to Zion:
   ransomed people homeward bound
      all your praises voicing,
   see your Lord with glory crowned,
      share in his rejoicing!

336
Kim Miller
© Parish of Eastbourne Trust Board, New Zealand †

1 When the Lord came to our land,
   he was not a wealthy man;
   he was born in poverty
   and the stars looked down to see:
      and the brightest star of all was his.
   Jesus was the Son of God,
   and he came to earth for me.

2 When the Lord came to our land,
   he was not a wealthy man;
   he was born in poverty
   and the angels came to see:
      and the angels sang their joyful news,
      and the brightest star of all was his.
   Jesus was the Son of God . . .

3 When the Lord came to our land,
   he was not a wealthy man;
   he was born in poverty
   and the shepherds came to see:
      and the shepherds
         knelt and worshipped him,
      and the angels sang their joyful news,
      and the brightest star of all was his.
   Jesus was the Son of God . . .

4 When the Lord came to our land,
  he was not a wealthy man;
  he was born in poverty
  and the wise men came to see:
    and the wise men brought rare gifts for him,
    and the shepherds
      knelt and worshipped him,
    and the angels sang their joyful news,
    and the brightest star of all was his.
  Jesus was the Son of God,
  and he came to earth for me.

5 When the Lord came to our land,
  he was not a wealthy man;
  he was born in poverty
  and the donkeys came to see:
    and the donkeys gave their stall for him,
    and the wise men brought rare gifts for him,
    and the shepherds
      knelt and worshipped him,
    and the angels sang their joyful news,
    and the brightest star of all was his.
  Jesus was the Son of God . . .

337

From Matthew 24
© Christopher Idle / Jubilate Hymns

1 When the sun is darkened
    and the moon gives no light
  and the stars fall from the sky,
  then in heaven will appear
    the long-promised sign
  that proclaims the Son of Man.

2 All the peoples of the world
    will cry and lament
  when they see the Son of Man
  coming in great power and glory
    high on the clouds
  with his angels serving him.

3 He will send his angels
    with a loud trumpet blast,
  from the farthest bounds of heaven;
  from the four winds they will gather
    his chosen ones
  who are ready for their Lord.

4 None on earth can prophesy
    the day or the hour
  which the Father knows alone:
  keep awake and well prepared,
    for Jesus will come
  at the time you least expect.

5 Happy is the servant
    who is found keeping faith
  when the master comes again;
  heaven and earth will pass away,
    but never the words
  of the Lord, the Son of Man.

338

© Timothy Dudley-Smith †

1 Where do Christmas songs begin?
  By the stable of an inn
  where the song of hosts on high
  mingled with a baby's cry.
  There, for joy and wonder, smiled
  man and maid and holy Child.
    Christmas songs begin with them:
    sing the songs of Bethlehem!

2 Who is this, whose human birth
  here proclaims him Child of earth?
  He it is who formed the skies,
  saw the new-made stars arise:
  Life immortal, Light divine,
  blinking in the candle-shine;
    born our darkness to dispel,
    God with us, Emmanuel!

3 Only love can answer why
  he should come to grieve and die,
  share on earth our pain and loss,
  bear for us the bitter cross.
  Love is come to seek and save,
  Life to master death and grave,
    so in Christ is all restored,
    risen and redeeming Lord!

4 Praise we then, in Christmas songs,
  him to whom all praise belongs.
  Hear the angel host reply
  'Glory be to God on high,
  joy and peace to mortals given,
  peace on earth and peace with heaven!'
    Join we now, as one with them:
    sing the songs of Bethlehem!

339

Al Vincent
© Lillenas Publishing Company / Thankyou Music †

S = SOLO, C = CONGREGATION

1 s Where's everybody going – please tell me?
  c Going to see a baby in-a Beth-a-lehem.
  s Why is everybody rushing – please tell me?
  c There's been a baby born in Beth-a-lehem.

2 s We've been a-looking for Mary and Joseph –
  c going to see a baby born in Beth-a-lehem.
  s Heard from an angel about a little baby,
  c born in a manger in-a Beth-a-lehem.

3 s Born in the Spirit, born in glory,
  c born in a manger in-a Beth-a-lehem.
  s Come from the Father – tell the story –
  c come down from heaven to-a Beth-a-lehem.

4 s Come to be our saviour – come in peace,
  c born in a manger in-a Beth-a-lehem.
  s Here to bring the prisoners release,
  c Jesus the saviour in-a Beth-a-lehem.

5 s See that star – it shines so bright,
  c shining on a manger in-a Beth-a-lehem.
  s Bring to earth such joy and light,
  c little baby Jesus born in Beth-a-lehem.

6 s God looked down from up above,
c gave to us a baby in-a Beth-a-lehem.
s Sent to us his perfect love,
c sent his son Jesus to Beth-a-lehem.

340 B R Hanby (1833–1867)

1 Who is he in yonder stall
at whose feet the shepherds fall?
It's the Lord – O, wondrous story!
It's the Lord, the king of glory!
At his feet we humbly fall –
crown him, crown him Lord of all!

2 Who is he in deep distress
fasting in the wilderness?
It's the Lord . . .

3 Who is he to whom they bring
all the sick and sorrowing?
It's the Lord . . .

4 Who is he the gathering throng
greet with loud triumphant song?
It's the Lord . . .

5 Who is he that on the tree
dies in shame and agony?
It's the Lord . . .

6 Who is he that from the grave
comes to heal and help and save?
It's the Lord . . .

7 Who is he that from his throne
rules through all the worlds alone?
It's the Lord . . .

341 N Tate (1652–1715)

1 While shepherds watched their flocks by night,
all seated on the ground,
the angel of the Lord came down
and glory shone around.

2 'Fear not,' said he – for mighty dread
had seized their troubled mind –
'Glad tidings of great joy I bring
to you and all mankind:

3 'To you in David's town this day
is born of David's line
a saviour, who is Christ the Lord.
And this shall be the sign:

4 'The heavenly babe you there shall find
to human view displayed,
all tightly wrapped in swathing bands
and in a manger laid.'

5 Thus spoke the seraph, and forthwith
appeared a shining throng
of angels praising God, who thus
addressed their joyful song:

6 'All glory be to God on high,
and to the earth be peace;
good will henceforth from highest heaven
begin and never cease!'

342 N Tate (1652–1715)

1 While shepherds watched their flocks by night,
all seated on the ground,
all seated on the ground,
the angel of the Lord came down
and glory shone around,
and glory shone around,
and glory shone around.

2 'Fear not,' said he – for mighty dread
had seized their troubled mind . . .
'Glad tidings of great joy I bring
to you and all mankind . . .

3 'To you in David's town this day
is born of David's line . . .
a saviour, who is Christ the Lord.
And this shall be the sign . . .

4 'The heavenly babe you there shall find
to human view displayed . . .
all tightly wrapped in swathing bands
and in a manger laid . . .

5 Thus spoke the seraph, and forthwith
appeared a shining throng . . .
of angels praising God, who thus
addressed their joyful song . . .

6 'All glory be to God on high,
and to the earth be peace . . .
good will henceforth from highest heaven
begin and never cease . . .

343 N Tate (1652–1715)

1 While shepherds watched their flocks by night,
all seated on the ground,
the angel of the Lord came down,
the angel of the Lord came down
and glory shone around,
and glory shone around,
and glory shone around.

2 'Fear not,' said he – for mighty dread
had seized their troubled mind –
'Glad tidings of great joy I bring,
glad tidings of great joy I bring
to you and all mankind . . .

3 'To you in David's town this day
is born of David's line
a saviour, who is Christ the Lord,
a saviour, who is Christ the Lord.
And this shall be the sign . . .

4 'The heavenly babe you there shall find
to human view displayed,
all tightly wrapped in swathing bands,
all tightly wrapped in swathing bands
and in a manger laid . . .

5 Thus spoke the seraph, and forthwith
appeared a shining throng
of angels praising God, who thus,
of angels praising God, who thus
addressed their joyful song . . .

6 'All glory be to God on high,
and to the earth be peace;
good will henceforth from highest heaven,
good will henceforth from highest heaven
begin and never cease . . .

344 N Tate (1652–1715)

1 SOLO
While shepherds watched their flocks by night,
all seated on the ground,
the angel of the Lord came down
and glory shone around.
ALL: shone around.

2 SOLO
'Fear not,' said he – for mighty dread
had seized their troubled mind –
'Glad tidings of great joy I bring
to you and all mankind:
ALL: all mankind:

3 ALL
'To you in David's town this day
is born of David's line
a saviour, who is Christ the Lord.
And this shall be the sign:

4 SOLO
'The heavenly babe you there shall find
to human view displayed,
all tightly wrapped in swathing bands
and in a manger laid.'
ALL: manger laid.'

5 ALL
Thus spoke the seraph, and forthwith
appeared a shining throng
of angels praising God, who thus
addressed their joyful song:

6 SOLO
'All glory be to God on high,
and to the earth be peace;
good will henceforth from highest heaven
begin and never cease!'
ALL: never cease,
never cease!'

345 From the French Unknown

1 Winds through the olive trees
softly did blow,
round little Bethlehem
long, long ago.

2 Sheep on the hillside lay,
white as the snow;
shepherds were watching them
long, long ago.

3 Then from the happy skies
angels bent low
singing their songs of joy
long, long ago:

4 For, in his manger bed
cradled, we know
Christ came to Bethlehem
long, long ago.

346 © Michael Perry / Jubilate Hymns

1 Who is this child that lies in humble splendour,
and spurns the night,
and braves the winter wild?
Was ever babe so lowly and so tender,
yet full of grace? Who is this little child?
This is the Christ, in whom we are forgiven;
this is the Lord, the mighty Son of Man;
this is our God,
who comes to us from heaven –
the living Word
who was before the world began!

2 What shall we sing to celebrate his story,
to praise our Lord and glorify our king?
How shall we tell the people of his glory,
and share his grace?
What shall his people sing?
This is the Christ . . .

347 © Christopher Idle / Jubilate Hymns

1 Wise men, they came to look for wisdom,
finding one wiser than they knew;
rich men, they met with one yet richer –
King of the kings, they knelt to you:
Jesus, our wisdom from above,
wealth and redemption, life and love.

2 Pilgrims they were, from unknown countries,
searching for one who knows the world;
lost are their names,
and strange their journeys,
famed is their zeal to find the child:
Jesus, in you the lost are claimed,
aliens are found, and known, and named.

3 Magi, they stooped to see your splendour,
led by a star to light supreme;
promised Messiah, Lord eternal,
glory and peace are in your name:
Joy of each day, our Song by night,
shine on our path your holy light.

4 Guests of their God, they opened treasures,
incense and gold and solemn myrrh,
welcoming one too young to question
how came these gifts, and what they were:
Gift beyond price of gold or gem,
make among us your Bethlehem.

348

1 Within a crib my saviour lay,
a wooden manger filled with hay,
come down for love on Christmas Day:
    all glory be to Jesus!

2 Upon a cross my saviour died,
to ransom sinners crucified,
his loving arms still open wide:
    all glory be to Jesus!

3 A victor's crown my saviour won,
his work of love and mercy done,
the Father's high-ascended Son:
    all glory be to Jesus!

349

From Isaiah 9
Bill Yarger

1 Wonderful Counsellor, Jesus:
search me, know me, Jesus;
lead me, guide me, Jesus –
Wonderful Counsellor, Jesus.

2 Mighty God, Son of God, Jesus;
name above all other names, Jesus:
glorify, magnify, Jesus –
Mighty God, Son of God, Jesus.

3 Everlasting Father, Jesus;
holy and unchangeable, Jesus:
fill me with your presence, Jesus –
Everlasting Father, Jesus.

4 Prince of peace, rule my heart, Jesus;
know my every anxious thought, Jesus;
calm my fears, dry my tears, Jesus –
Prince of peace, rule my heart, Jesus.

5 Wonderful Counsellor, Jesus;
Mighty God, Son of God, Jesus;
Everlasting Father, Jesus –
Prince of peace, rule my heart, Jesus!

350/351

1 Word of the Father everlasting,
there at his side when time began;
who but the Word reflects his glory,
who but the Word may speak to man?
    Word of the Father everlasting,
    there at his side when time began.

2 Word once made flesh in Mary's keeping,
source of all life and one true light;
who of his own will dare receive him,
or to their homes and hearts invite?
    Word once made flesh in Mary's keeping,
    source of all life and one true light.

3 Word full of grace, among us dwelling,
Jesus our Lord, the Father's Son:
give us the power, your name confessing,
truly God's children to become.
    Word full of grace, among us dwelling,
    Jesus our Lord, the Father's Son.

352

From Isaiah 9
Mavis Ford

You are the King of glory,
you are the Prince of peace,
you are the Lord of heaven and earth,
you're the Sun of righteousness!
Angels bow down before you,
worship and adore,
for you have the words of eternal life –
you are Jesus Christ the Lord!
    Hosanna to the Son of David,
    hosanna to the King of kings:
    glory in the highest heaven,
    for Jesus the Messiah reigns!
    Hosanna . . .

353

From Luke 12
P Doddridge (1702–1751)

1 You servants of the Lord
who for his coming wait:
observe with care his heavenly word –
be watchful at his gate.

2 Let all your lamps be bright
and guard the living flame;
be ready always in his sight,
for awesome is his name.

3 Await your Lord's command –
the bridegroom shall appear:
for his returning is at hand,
and while we speak he's near.

4 O happy servants they
who wide awake are found
to greet their master on that day,
and be with honour crowned!

5 Christ shall the banquet spread
with his own royal hand,
and raise each faithful servant's head
amid the angelic band.

354

Isaiah 55
Stuart Dauermann

You shall go out with joy
and be led forth in peace;
and the mountains and the hills
shall break forth before you,
singing songs of joy,
and the trees of the field
shall clap, shall clap their hands;
    and the trees of the field
        shall clap their hands,
    and the trees of the field
        shall clap their hands,
    and the trees of the field
        shall clap their hands,
as you go out with joy!

355

F L Hosmer (1840–1928)
© in this version Word & Music / Jubilate Hymns

1 Your kingdom come! On bended knee
   through passing years we pray:
  all faithful people long to see
   on earth that kingdom's day.

2 The hours of waiting through the night
   no less to God belong;
  the stars declare the eternal right
   and shame the creature's wrong.

3 And there already in the skies
   the dawn's first rays appear –
  you prophets of our God, arise,
   proclaim the day is near:

4 The day in whose clear shining light
   the Lord shall stand revealed,
  and every wrong be turned to right,
   and every hurt be healed:

5 When justice joined with truth and peace
   make straight the Saviour's road –
  the day of perfect righteousness,
   the promised day of God!

ACKNOWLEDGEMENTS

We thank all those who contributed to the compilation of *Carol Praise*:

The 'Jubilate Hymns' team for the application of their immense expertise – especially in this case Noël Tredinnick, Norman Warren and Clifford Roseweir.

The 'Word & Music' team – especially Bunty Grundy and her assistants, Ann Darlington and Sylvia Bleasdale, for their efficiency and skill in getting material ready for publication.

The 'Marshalls' team – notably Debbie Thorpe, Stanley Grant, Jim Girling, and Tim Sanders – for believing in us before we sell the first million!

Our long-suffering wives, Beatrice and Jane, who have been enduring Christmas solidly for three years.

And we are grateful to all who have bought this book in order to share the vision of proclaiming Christ to the world at the season when hearts are most readily open to receive him.

Michael Perry and David Peacock

LEGAL INFORMATION

ADDRESSES

From which permission to reproduce copyright items
should be obtained

A & C Black, Howard Road, Eaton Scoton, Huntingdon, Cambridgeshire PE19 3EZ

Anfield Music Ltd, 201 Monument Road, Edgbaston, Birmingham, B16 8UU

Berea College, Berea, Kentucky 40404, USA

Bible Society, Stonehill Green, Westlea, Swindon, SN5 7DG

Blandford Press, Link House, West Street, Poole, Dorset BH15 1LL

Boosey & Hawkes, 295 Regent Street, London W1R 8JH

Bourne Music, 34/36 Maddox Street, London W1R 9PD

Breitkopf und Hartel, Buch und Musikverlag, Walkmuhlstrasse 52, Wiesbaden 1, West Germany

Cherry Lane Music (and Cherry Pie Music), 75 High Street, Needham Market, Ipswich, Suffolk IP6 8AW

Christian Fellowship of Columbia, 4600 Christian Fellowship Road, Columbia, Missouri 65203, USA

Clifton Music, Clifton Cathedral House, Clifton Park, Bristol BS8 3BX

Columbia Pictures Music, 3500 West Olive Avenue, Burbank, California 91505, USA

Coronation Music, c/o 32 St Alban's Road, Westbury Park, Bristol BS6 7ST

Ears & Eyes Music, Kerygma House, Canal Road, Leeds LS12 2PL

Glory Alleluia Music, Tempo Music Publications, 2712 W 104th Terrace, Leawood, Kansas 66206, USA

Gordon V Thompson Music Ltd, 29 Birch Avenue, Toronto, Ontario M4V 1E2, Canada

High-Fye Music, c/o Campbell Connelly, 8–9 Frith Street, London W1V 5TZ

Hodder & Stoughton, 47 Bedford Square, London WC1B 3DP

Hope Publishing Company, Carol Stream, Illinois 60188, USA

Hymns Ancient and Modern, St Mary's Works, St Mary's Plain, Norwich, Norfolk NR3 3BH

Integrity's Hosanna! Music, Integrity Communications, PO Box Z, Mobile, Al. 36616 USA

International Music Publications, Woodford Trading Estate, Southend Road, Woodford Green, Essex IG8 8HN

Josef Weinberger, 12/14 Mortimer Street, London W1N 7RD

Jubilate Hymns Ltd, c/o 61 Chessel Avenue, Bitterne, Southampton SO2 4DY

Lindsay Music, 23 Hitchin Street, Biggleswade, Bedfordshire SG18 8AX

Magnificat Music, St Thomas More Centre, 9 Henry Road, Brownswood Park, London N4 2LH

Mustard Seed Music, 9 Holdom Avenue, Bletchley, Milton Keynes MK1 1QU

New Song Ministries, PO Box 11662, Costa Mesa, California 92627 USA

Overseas Missionary Fellowship, Belmont, The Vine, Sevenoaks, Kent

Oxford University Press (London), Ely House, 37 Dover Street, London W1X 4AH

Oxford University Press (Oxford), Walton Street, Oxford OX2 6DP

Parish of Eastbourne Trust, PO Box 41026, Eastbourne, Wellington, New Zealand

Religious and Moral Education Press, Hennock Road, Exeter EX2 8RP

Renewal Servicing, PO Box 366, Addlestone, Weybridge, Surrey KT15 3UL

Restoration Music Ltd, Harvestime House, 136 Hall Lane, Bradford, West Yorkshire BD4 7DG

Royal School of Church Music, Addington Palace, Croydon, Surrey CR9 5AD

Salvationist Publishing and Supplies Ltd, 117/121 Judd Street, Kings Cross, London WC1H 9NN

St Paul's Outreach Trust, PO Box 6349, Wellesley Street, Auckland 1, New Zealand

Stainer & Bell Ltd, 82 High Road, London N2 9PW

Thankyou Music, PO Box 75, Eastbourne, East Sussex BN23 6NW

Tree International, 8 Music Square West, PO Box 1273, Nashville, Tennessee 37203, USA

Tro Essex Music Ltd, Essex House, 19/20 Poland Street, London W1V 3DD

William Elkin Music Services, Station Road Industrial Estate, Salhouse, Norwich, Norfolk NR13 6NY

Word & Music, c/o Jubilate Hymns, 61 Chessel Avenue, Bitterne, Southampton SO2 4DY

Word Music (UK), 9 Holdom Avenue, Bletchley, Milton Keynes MK1 1QU

Word of God Music, PO Box 8617, 840 Airport Blvd, Ann Arbor, Michigan 48107, USA

FURTHER COPYRIGHT INFORMATION

relating to copyright ascriptions marked † in the text

1 Used by permission of A & C Black (publishers) Ltd
2 Used by permission of Magnificat Music
9 Words: administered in North America by Hope Publishing Company
12 © 1981 Glory Alleluia Music. International copyright secured. All rights reserved. Used by permission only
15 © 1978 Thankyou Music
16 Music: Composer and copyright-holder sought
17 Copyright-holder sought
18 Used by permission of Magnificat Music
19 © 1975 administered in Europe by Thankyou Music
23 Arrangement and descant: used by permission of the Royal School of Church Music
24 © 1982 Thankyou Music
26 Music: © 1974 Chappell Music Ltd, London W1Y 3FA. Reproduced by permission of Chappell Music Ltd and International Music Publications
28 © administered by Religious and Moral Education Press
31 © 1984 Thankyou Music
32 Music: reprinted by permission of Gordon V Thompson Music, Toronto, Canada
35 Music arrangement: copyright-holder sought
36 Author and composer sought
40 © 1964/1987, used by permission of Stainer & Bell Ltd. A leaflet version for SSSA is published and available from them
45 Music arrangement used by permission of Oxford University Press (London)
50 Used by permission of Oxford University Press (Oxford)
53 Music: © 1961, 1987, used by permission of Stainer & Bell Ltd
55 © 1974 Chappell Music Ltd, London W1Y 3FA. Reproduced by permission of Chappell Music Ltd and International Music Publications
60 © Christopher Walker / Clifton Music. Adapted and used by permission
61 © 1972, and music arrangement © 1987 High-Fye Music Ltd. Used by permission. All rights reserved
65 © 1981 Thankyou Music
66 © 1981 Thankyou Music
68 Used by permission of Ears and Eyes Production Company Ltd
69 © 1984 Thankyou Music
72 Words: administered in North America by Hope Publishing Company. Music: used by kind permission of Breitkopf and Hartel, Wiesbaden
73 © 1975 administered in Europe by Thankyou Music
74 Used by permission of Magnificat Music
76 © 1985 Thankyou Music

78 Copyright-holder sought
79 © 1985 Thankyou Music
80 © 1979 Thankyou Music
81 © 1976 administered by Word Music (UK) (A division of Word (UK) Ltd)
83 Words: administered in North America by Hope Publishing Company
84 © 1985 Word Music (UK) (A division of Word (UK) Ltd)
86 Music: used by permission of Hymns Ancient & Modern Ltd
88 © 1985 Thankyou Music
89 © 1984 Restoration Music Ltd
91 © 1983 Thankyou Music
92 © Bible Society
93 Words: administered in North America by Hope Publishing Company
94 Words: used by permission of Oxford University Press (Oxford)
97 © 1980 Lesley Neal
98 © Glory Alleluia Music. International copyright secured. All rights reserved. Used by permission only
101 © 1982 Word Music (UK) (A division of Word (UK) Ltd)
102 © 1984 Thankyou Music
103 © 1966 Willard F Jabusch, St Mary of the Lake, Mundelein, Illinois 60060, USA
104 © 1982 Thankyou Music
106 Music: © 1954 Chappell Music Ltd, London W1Y 3FA. Reproduced by permission of Chappell Music Ltd and International Music Publications
116 © 1983 administered in Europe by Thankyou Music
117 © 1980 administered by Word Music (UK) (A division of Word (UK) Ltd)
118 Words: author sought
119 © 1978 Thankyou Music
120 Used by permission of Cherry Lane Music Ltd
121 Words: administered in North America by Hope Publishing Company
123 Words: administered in North America by Hope Publishing Company
124 Words: administered in North America by Hope Publishing Company
125 © 1974, 1978 Thankyou Music
127 Words: administered in North America by Hope Publishing Company
130 © 1984 Integrity's Hosanna! Music. All rights reserved. International copyright secured. Used by permission only
133 © 1984 Mustard Seed Music
136 © 1973 administered in Europe by Thankyou Music
142 Music: used by permission of Berea College, Kentucky

'STORY' INDEX TO CAROLS

The full index including first lines
appears in the Music Edition of Carol Praise

He's coming!

The promise – 49, 106, 203, 221, 230, 236, 268, 270, 279, 301, 354

The appearance – 24, 31, 32, 93, 144

The reign – 36, 55, 56, 57, 88, 98, 102, 104, 125, 145, 217, 284, 299, 315, 325, 352

The longing – 67, 70, 159, 170, 209, 249, 355

The deliverer – 62, 76, 156/157, 161, 162, 163, 247, 335, 349

The alarm – 18, 20, 37, 92, 199, 200, 241, 242, 243, 280, 337, 353

The welcome – 86, 113, 125, 147, 148, 164, 234, 271, 273, 287, 312

The delight – 153, 158, 197, 232

His birth is foretold

Mary is told – 8, 174, 194, 204, 286, 334

Mary rejoices – 195/196, 201, 285

Joseph is told – 22, 79, 80, 81, 149, 246

Zechariah blesses God – 205, 211, 229, 240

The time comes

The journey to Bethlehem – 172, 174, 175, 202, 222, 282, 294, 314

The stable – 118, 142, 151, 255, 293, 316, 317, 338

Jesus is born

The baby – 3/4, 5, 38/39, 40, 42, 44/45, 89, 123/124, 126, 134, 137, 139, 169, 186, 207, 259, 289/290, 346

The mother – 46, 95/96, 193

The crib – 25–27, 43, 73, 135, 228, 340, 348

The lullabies – 28, 127, 129, 150, 189, 190, 258, 274, 276, 283

The rejoicing – 52, 107, 112, 114, 117, 245, 265, 288, 330

The birth is proclaimed

The silent night – 33, 213–216, 266, 322

The good news – 60, 85, 87, 264, 310

The shepherds and the angels – 138, 308, 324, 333, 341–344

The angels' song – 47, 90, 97, 115, 122, 174, 178, 183, 311, 345

The message of peace – 6, 140/141, 218

The celebration – 9, 13, 14, 63, 77, 111, 121, 224, 227, 233, 256, 332

We join in – 16, 21, 152, 165, 272, 319

Come to worship

Come to Bethlehem – 48, 59, 72, 171, 181, 206, 210, 212, 220, 262, 263, 309, 339

At the stable – 7, 58, 108, 110, 116, 143, 173, 185, 237, 257, 263, 281, 297, 305, 326, 327

The worship – 34, 51, 53, 94, 120, 136, 192, 251, 269, 277, 300, 304, 328

Everybody must know

The wise men set out – 35, 50, 71, 155, 248, 250, 308

The star guides them – 78, 132, 212, 267, 275, 302

They offer gifts – 1, 10, 41, 64, 191, 225, 244, 321, 347

They offer homage – 12, 23, 61, 65, 66, 99, 100, 113, 208, 219, 239, 254, 298, 313, 329

We respond with our gifts – 11, 130, 306, 323, 331

We respond with our praise – 177, 252, 260, 261, 291, 292, 303, 333

We tell everyone – 103, 109, 160, 168, 231, 253, 318, 320

Jesus' life is threatened

The refugee – 128, 146, 176, 182, 223, 278

Jesus is recognised . .

. . by Simeon – 83, 147, 179, 180

. . by John the Baptist – 226

. . by us – 19, 54, 74, 101, 105, 133, 148, 238, 350/351

We wonder at God's love

From riches to poverty – 15, 91, 167, 184, 187/188, 207, 293, 296

From heaven to earth – 29/30, 38/39, 75, 82, 102, 169, 198, 257, 289–290, 336

From paradise to pain – 2, 3/4, 131, 186, 295, 340, 346, 348

We sing his praise

Alleluia! – 17, 68, 69, 84, 119, 154, 166, 235, 307, 349, 352

INDEX TO BIBLE REFERENCES

The full text including first lines
appears in the Music Edition of Carol Praise

MAIN INDEX

Italics indicate translations, versions and titles

Born in the night – 40
Bread of life, hope of the world (A child is born for us) – 2
Brightest and best of the suns of the morning – 41

Calypso Carol (See him lying on a bed of straw) – 257
Camel Shuffle, The (Riding out across the desert) – 250
Candles and crowns (Sent away to a cattle shed) – 255
Caribbean Carol (Long ago and far away) – 173
Carol of the Drum (Soldiers marching) – 278
Cherry Tree Carol (As Joseph was awaking) – 22
Child in a stable – 43
Child in the manger – 42
Child of gladness, child of sorrow – 44/45
Christ is born for us today – 46
Christ is born to be our king – 47
Christ is born within a stable – 48
Christ is surely coming – 49
Christ was born on Christmas Day – 50
Christians, awake – 51
Christians, make a joyful sound – 52
Christmas for God's holy people – 53
Christmas news – 54
Christmas Procession (Come and hear the news) – 60
Clap your hands – 55
Clap your hands, you people – 56
Clothed in kingly majesty – 57
Come all you good people – 58
Come and hear the joyful singing – 59
Come and hear the news – 60
Come and join the celebration – 61
Come and praise the Lord our king – 64
Come and see the shining hope – 62
Come and sing the Christmas story – 63
Come now with awe – 72
Come O long-expected Jesus – 70
Come on, let us sing to the Lord – 69
Come ride with kings – 71
Come, they told me (Soldiers marching) – 278
Come to set us free – 74
Come, let us glorify the Lord – 65
Come, let us kneel before him – 66
Come, let us worship our redeemer – 68
Come, Lord Jesus – 67
Communion Song (Jesus, Lamb of God) – 148
Coventry Carol (Hush, do not cry) – 128
Cradle rocking, cattle lowing – 73
Crucifer (Fling wide the gates) – 86

Dambusters March (God is our strength and refuge) – 106
Dans cette etable (Child in a stable) – 43
Darkness like a shroud covers the earth – 76
Deck the hall with boughs of holly (Come and hear the joyful singing) – 59
Ding Dong! Merrily on high – 77
Ding, dong, ring out the carillon – 78
Down from the height – 75

Light shining in the darkness – 167
Light the candles round the world – 168
Lights to the world (The earth was dark until you spoke) – 291
Like a flicker in the darkness – 169
Lion of Judah, on the throne – 170
Little children, wake and listen – 171
Little donkey, little donkey – 172
Little Jesus, sweetly sleep (Jesus, saviour, holy child) – 150
Living under the shadow of his wing – 166
Londonderry Air (Who is this child) – 346
Long ago and far away – 173
Long, long ago it happened – 174
Long time ago in Bethlehem – 175
Look away to Bethlehem – 177
Look to the skies, there's a celebration – 178
Lord everlasting – 176
Lord, now let your servant depart in peace – 179
Lord, now let your servant go his own way in peace – 180
Lord, speak softly to my soul – 181
Lord, who left the highest heaven – 182
Lord, you left your throne – 183
Lord, you were rich beyond all splendour – 184
Love came down at Christmas – 187/188
Love is come again (Mary came with meekness) – 191
Love was born at Christmas – 186
Lowly Jesus, king of glory – 185
Lullaby, baby, lie still and slumber – 190
Lullaby, little Jesus – 189
Lullay, lullay, thou little tiny child (Hush, do not cry) – 128

Magnificat/The Song of Mary
       (Mary sang a song, a song of love) – 195/196
       (My soul glorifies the Lord) – 201
       (Tell out, my soul, the greatness of the Lord) – 285
Make way, make way for Christ the king – 197
Marching through Georgia (Come and see the shining hope) – 62
Mary and Joseph – praise with them – 192
Mary came with meekness – 191
Mary had a baby, yes Lord – 193
Mary, listen to the angel of the Lord – 194
Mary sang a song, a song of love – 195/196
Mary's boy child (Long time ago in Bethlehem) – 175
Mary's child (Born in the night) – 40
Meekness and majesty – 198
Michael, row the boat ashore (Come and praise the Lord our king) – 64
Mighty in victory, glorious in majesty – 199
My Lord, he is a-coming soon – 200
My soul glorifies the Lord – 201

New Wine (One shall tell another) – 230
No room for the baby (No room for the saviour) – 202
No room for the saviour – 202
No small wonder (Small wonder the star) – 261
No weapon formed, or army or king – 203
Noël nouvelet (Mary came with meekness) – 191
Now tell us, gentle Mary – 204

Quittez pasteurs (O leave your sheep) – 212

Rejoice and be merry – 244
Rejoice, rejoice, a saviour has come – 246
Rejoice, rejoice! Christ is in you – 247
Rejoice, rejoice, for the king Messiah's born – 248
Rejoice with heart and voice – 245
Resonet in laudibus (Christ is born for us today) – 46
Resonet in laudibus (Christians, make a joyful sound) – 52
Restore, O Lord, the honour of your name – 249
Riding out across the desert – 250
Ring, bells of Bethlehem – 252
Ring out the bells – 251
Ring the bells, ring the bells – 253
Rise up, shepherd, and follow (There's a saviour to see on Christmas morn) – 309
Rocking Carol (Jesus, saviour, holy child) – 150
Royal sons of a royal king – 254

Sans Day Carol (When the angel came to Mary) – 334
See, amid the winter snow – 256
See him lying on a bed of straw – 257
See the dawn appearing – 258
See, to us a child is born – 259
Sent away to a cattle shed – 255
Shepherds came, their praises bringing – 260
Shepherds in the fields abiding (Angels from the realms of glory) – 21
Shepherds' Journey (Off to David's town they go) – 220
Shepherds, leave your drowsy sheep – 262
Shepherds, leave your flocks – 263
Shepherds, wake to news of joy – 264
Shout aloud, girls and boys – 265
Silent night! holy night – 266
Silver star shining out over Bethlehem – 267
Sing a new song of thanksgiving – 268
Sing a new song to the Lord – 271
Sing a song, a joyful song – 269
Sing alleluia to the Lord – 270
Sing glory, glory – 272
Sing heaven, shout for joy – 273
Sing lullaby – 274
Skye Boat Song (Hush, little baby; peace, little boy) – 129
Small wonder the star – 261
Soft the evening shadows fall – 275
Softly, a shepherd is singing – 276
Soldiers marching – 278
Songs of gladness, songs of gladness – 277
Soon – and very soon – 279
Sound loud the trumpet (Lift up your hearts to the Lord) – 164
Sound on the trumpet – 280
Standing in the rain – 282
Star bright (If I'd been there in Bethlehem) – 132
Still, still, still – 281
Sussex Carol (Good Christian people, rise and sing) – 111
Sweet Chiming Christmas Bells (The bells ring out at Christmas-time) – 288
Sweet was the song that Mary sang – 283